ST(P) MATHEMATICS 3B

ST(P) MATHEMATICS 3B

L. Bostock, B.Sc.

S. Chandler, B.Sc.

A. Shepherd, B.Sc.

E. Smith, M.Sc.

Second Edition

Stanley Thornes (Publishers) Ltd

First published in 1985 by:
Stanley Thornes (Publishers) Ltd
Old Station Drive
Leckhampton
CHELTENHAM GL53 0DN
England

Reprinted 1986
Reprinted 1987
Second edition 1991
Reprinted 1992 (twice)

British Library Cataloguing in Publication Data
ST(P) mathematics. 2nd ed.
   Book 3B
   1. Mathematics
   I. Bostock, L.
   510

ISBN 0 7487 0544 9

Typeset by Tech-Set, Gateshead, Tyne & Wear.
Printed and bound in Great Britain at The Bath Press, Avon.

CONTENTS

INTRODUCTION

This book is part of the ST(P) graded series in mathematics. It is intended for use in the third year of secondary schools. It should enable you to achieve about Level 6 of the National Curriculum in mathematics for Key Stage 3. Some of the work in this book goes beyond Level 6; this is in preparation for Key Stage 4 at the age of 16 plus. Books 4B and 5B continue to develop the mathematics necessary to reach about Level 7/8 at GCSE.

As is the case with the earlier books in this series there are plenty of straightforward questions. The exercises are divided into three types of question.

The first type, identified by plain numbers, e.g. **12.**, help you to see if you understand the work. These questions are considered necessary for every chapter you attempt.

The second type, identified by a single underline, e.g. **12.**, are extra, but not harder, questions for quicker workers, for extra practice or for later revision.

The third type, identified by a double underline, e.g. **12.**, are for those of you who manage type 1 questions fairly easily and therefore need to attempt slightly harder questions.

Most chapters end with mixed exercises and the book ends with some multiple choice revision exercises. These will help you revise what you have done, at a later date.

You will notice that the position of the decimal point has been lowered to conform with the general standard of mathematical and scientific typesetting.

1 NUMBER WORK

This chapter summarises what you should already know and adds some new processes.

Use a calculator as little as possible in this chapter, except in Exercise 1n. You should use one only if you get stuck or to check some of the more complicated arithmetic.

PLACE VALUE AND SIZES OF NUMBERS

EXERCISE 1a

What is the value of each 3 in the number 323 ?

The value of the first 3 is 3 hundreds, i.e. 300.

The value of the second 3 is 3 units (or just 3).

1. What is the value of the 5 in the number 6542 ?

2. What is the value of each 7 in the number 7207 ?

3. Find the difference between the place values of the two 4's in the number 3445.

4. Give the number that follows 999.

5. Which is greater, 303 or 36 ?

6. a) Form as many three-figure numbers as you can from the figures 2 and 5. You may use each figure as many times as you please, so 222 is a possible number.
b) Put your numbers in order of size, lowest first.

7. Write in words the number   a) 4782   b) 1 000 000.

1

8. Write in figures the number
  a) two hundred and three
  b) a thousand and seventy-eight.

9. How many hundreds are there in
  a) 600   b) 6000   c) 6200?

10. How many tens are there in
  a) 80   b) 180   c) 800?

11. Write in words the number
  a) 127
  b) 3789.

PRIME NUMBERS

A number that can be divided exactly only by itself and 1 is called a prime number;
e.g. 7 is a prime number (because 7 can only be 7×1)
but 6 is not a prime number (because $6 = 6 \times 1$ or 3×2).

The smallest prime number is 2, as 1 is *not* a prime number.

EXERCISE 1b   **1.** Write down the first four prime numbers.

2. Write down all the prime numbers that are less than 12.

3. Write down the prime numbers that are between 12 and 20.

4. In the set {2, 3, 4, 5, 6, 7, 8}, which members are prime numbers?

5. In the set {5, 7, 9, 11, 13, 15}, which members are prime numbers?

6. In the set {20, 21, 22, 23, 24, 25}, which members are prime numbers?

7. Apart from 2, are there any even numbers that are prime numbers?

FACTORS

A factor of a number divides exactly into that number, e.g. 2 is a factor of 10 because 2 divides into 10 exactly 5 times.

On the other hand 3 is not a factor of 10 because 3 does not divide exactly into 10.

EXERCISE 1c

1. Is 2 a factor of
    a) 4   b) 9   c) 12   d) 21   e) 84?

2. How can you tell whether 2 is a factor of a number greater than 10?

3. Is 5 a factor of
    a) 8   b) 10   c) 15   d) 21   e) 85?

4. How can you tell whether 5 is a factor of a number?

5. Write down those numbers of the set {8, 16, 40, 35, 41, 515, 206} for which   a) 2 is a factor   b) 5 is a factor.

6. Is 3 a factor of
    a) 6   b) 9   c) 10   d) 15   e) 16?

7. The number 3 is a factor of 51. Add the digits of 51.
Is 3 a factor of your answer?

8. The numbers 75 and 102 are each divisible by 3.
    a) Add the digits of 75. Is your answer divisible by 3?
    b) Add the digits of 102. Is your answer divisible by 3?
    c) What conclusion do you come to? Test your idea on other numbers.

From the last exercise we see that

> any number ending in an even number is divisible by 2
> any number ending in 0 or 5 is divisible by 5
> when the sum of the digits of a number is divisible by 3,
> the number itself is divisible by 3

EXERCISE 1d

Write down all the factors of 12.

1, 2, 3, 4, 6, 12 are all factors of 12.

(Note that factors of a number are not always prime.)

Write down all the factors of

1. 6	**5.** 9	**9.** 21
2. 8	**6.** 18	**10.** 26
3. 10	**7.** 15	**11.** 51
4. 4	**8.** 19	**12.** 16

13. a) Write down all the factors of 24.
b) Which of the factors are prime numbers?

PRIME FACTORS

Sometimes we need to know just the prime factors of a number and to be able to express the number as the product of its prime factors.

For example, the prime factors of 6 are 2 and 3

and $6 = 2 \times 3$

For larger numbers we need an organised approach.

Consider the number 84.

The lowest prime factor of 84 is 2,
so we divide 84 by 2 $84 \div 2 = 42$
We then repeat the process with 42 $42 \div 2 = 21$

We repeat the process with 21
but this time 3 is the lowest prime factor of 21 $21 \div 3 = 7$

The next prime to try is 5 but 5 is
not a factor of 7. Try 7 $7 \div 7 = 1$

Therefore as a product of its prime factors,

$$84 = 2 \times 2 \times 3 \times 7$$

It is easier to keep track of the prime factors if the division is set out like this:

$$\begin{array}{r|r} 2 & 84 \\ \hline 2 & 42 \\ \hline 3 & 21 \\ \hline 7 & 7 \\ \hline & 1 \end{array}$$

WE MUST CARRY ON DIVIDING UNTIL WE GET 1 HERE.

EXERCISE 1e

Express 90 as the product of its prime factors.

$90 = 2 \times 3 \times 3 \times 5$

$$\begin{array}{r|r} 2 & 90 \\ \hline 3 & 45 \\ \hline 3 & 15 \\ \hline 5 & 5 \\ \hline & 1 \end{array}$$

Express the following numbers as products of their prime factors.

1.	10	**4.**	12	**7.**	60	**10.**	66
2.	21	**5.**	8	**8.**	50	**11.**	126
3.	35	**6.**	28	**9.**	36	**12.**	108

MULTIPLES

If a number divides exactly into another number, the second is a multiple of the first.

For example, the first six multiples of 3 are   3, 6, 9, 12, 15, 18

EXERCISE 1f   **1.**   From the set   {2, 3, 5, 6, 8, 10, 12, 14, 15, 16, 18, 20}   write down the numbers which are

a) multiples of 2   d) multiples of 5
b) multiples of 3   e) multiples of 6
c) multiples of 4   f) multiples of 8

2.   Write down the first four multiples of

a) 7   b) 5   c) 8   d) 10   e) 12   f) 15

3. Write down the multiples of 9 between 50 and 100.

4. Write down the multiples of 7 between 10 and 50.

SQUARES

A square number, or perfect square, can be written as the product of two equal numbers.

For example, 16 is a perfect square because $16 = 4 \times 4$

EXERCISE 1g **1.** Write down all the square numbers between 2 and 10.

2. Write down the perfect squares between 10 and 101.

3. In the set $\{2, 4, 6, 8, 10, 12, 16, 20\}$ which members are square numbers?

4. In the set $\{2, 4, 8, 16, 32, 64, 128\}$ which members are perfect squares?

MULTIPLYING A STRING OF NUMBERS

Consider $2 \times 3 \times 6$; this means multiply 2 by 3 and then multiply the result by 6.

$$2 \times 3 \times 6 = 6 \times 6$$
$$= 36$$

Notice that for multiplication we can change the order if we wish,

i.e. $$2 \times 6 \times 5 = 12 \times 5$$
$$= 60$$

or $$2 \times 6 \times 5 = 2 \times 5 \times 6$$
$$= 10 \times 6$$
$$= 60$$

EXERCISE 1h Calculate

1.	$2 \times 3 \times 4$	**5.**	$2 \times 5 \times 2 \times 3$	**9.**	$3 \times 5 \times 2$
2.	$3 \times 2 \times 5$	**6.**	$4 \times 2 \times 4 \times 3$	**10.**	$4 \times 5 \times 3$
3.	$5 \times 4 \times 2$	**7.**	$3 \times 7 \times 1 \times 5$	**11.**	$6 \times 2 \times 3$
4.	$7 \times 2 \times 2$	**8.**	$5 \times 2 \times 3 \times 4$	**12.**	$3 \times 7 \times 2$

INDEX NOTATION

In the number 2^3, the small 3 is called an index number, or power, and 2^3 means $2 \times 2 \times 2$.

We read 2^3 as "2 to the power of 3", or "2 cubed".

In the same way, $4 \times 4 \times 4 \times 4 \times 4$ can be written as 4^5.

We say "4 to the power 5" or "4 to the fifth power", or "4 to the fifth" for short.

3×3 is 3^2 and we say "3 squared".

EXERCISE 1i Find the value of

1. 2^2	**5.** 5^2	**9.** 7^2
2. 3^3	**6.** 4^3	**10.** 2^3
3. 4^2	**7.** 5^3	**11.** 4^4
4. 2^4	**8.** 3^4	**12.** 6^3

13. Find the value of   a) 2^5 b) 3^2 c) $2^5 \times 3^2$

14. Find the value of $3^3 \times 2^2$

MIXED OPERATIONS

When a calculation involves a mixture of brackets, addition, subtraction, multiplication and division, we always deal first with whatever is in the brackets.

Next we do the multiplication and division and lastly the addition and subtraction.

For example $3 + 4 \times 2 = 3 + 8 = 11$

but $(3 + 4) \times 2 = 7 \times 2 = 14$

It helps if brackets are put round the parts that are to be done first; we can write $3 + 4 \times 2$ as $3 + (4 \times 2)$ so that we know where to start.

Remember that the sign $\times$, $+$, $-$ or $\div$, applies only to the number that follows it.

EXERCISE 1j

Calculate   a) $6 \div 2 + 4 \times 2$ b) $18 - (2 + 4) \times 2$

a) $6 \div 2 + 4 \times 2 = (6 \div 2) + (4 \times 2)$

$$= 3 + 8$$

$$= 11$$

b) $18 - (2 + 4) \times 2 = 18 - 6 \times 2$

$$= 18 - 12$$

$$= 6$$

Calculate

1. $8 - 2 \times 2$

2. $3 \times 4 - 6$

3. $5 + 2 \times 3$

4. $10 \div 2 + 2$

5. $3 + 4 - 6 \div 3$

6. $2 \times 7 + 8 \div 4$

<u>7.</u> $3 + 1 \times 3 - 2$

<u>8.</u> $14 - 2 \times 4 + 7$

<u>9.</u> $12 \div 4 + 3 \times 2$

10. $3 \times (2 + 4)$

11. $(4 + 6) \times 2$

12. $(3 + 1) \times (3 + 2)$

13. $(8 - 5) \div 3$

14. $(6 - 1) \times 2$

15. $(14 - 6) \div 2$

<u>16.</u> $(8 - 4) \div (3 - 1)$

<u>17.</u> $9 \div (6 - 3)$

<u>18.</u> $9 \times (6 - 3)$

19. $4 \times 2 + 3$

20. $4 \times (2 + 3)$

21. $3 \times 2 - 2 \div 2$

22. $10 - 6 - 2 + 3$

23. $5 - 1 \times 3 - 2$

24. $(5 - 1) \times (3 - 2)$

<u>25.</u> $5 - 1 \times (3 - 2)$

<u>26.</u> $(5 - 1) \times 3 - 2$

<u>27.</u> $9 \div 3 + 9 \times 3$

EXERCISE 1k

Calculate   a) $\dfrac{3 + 5}{6 - 2}$ b) $\dfrac{3}{6} + \dfrac{5}{2}$

a) $\dfrac{3 + 5}{6 - 2} = \dfrac{8}{4}$

$$= 2$$

b) $\dfrac{3}{6} + \dfrac{5}{2} = \dfrac{1}{2} + 2\dfrac{1}{2}$

$$= 3$$

Calculate

1. $\dfrac{2+4}{1+3}$ **4.** $\dfrac{2+3}{2}$ **7.** $6+\dfrac{6}{3}$

2. $\dfrac{14}{3+4}$ **5.** $\dfrac{6}{5-2}$ **8.** $\dfrac{6+6}{3}$

3. $2+\dfrac{3}{2}$ **6.** $\dfrac{9}{4}-2$ **9.** $\dfrac{6}{6+3}$

If we are asked to work out $4-6$ we find that the answer is a negative number.

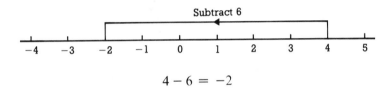

$$4 - 6 = -2$$

We can add and subtract more than two numbers.

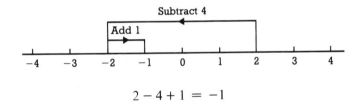

$$2 - 4 + 1 = -1$$

EXERCISE 1I

Find $-3 + 4 - 5$

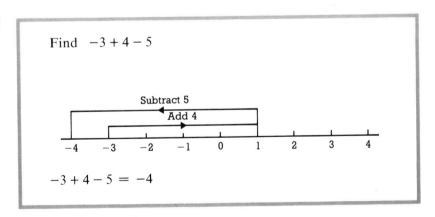

$$-3 + 4 - 5 = -4$$

1. Find
a) $-2 + 6$ b) $3 - 5$ c) $2 - 3 + 4$

Use this number line, if needed, to calculate the answers.

$$\underset{-10\ -9\ -8\ -7\ -6\ -5\ -4\ -3\ -2\ -1\ \ 0\ \ 1\ \ 2\ \ 3\ \ 4\ \ 5\ \ 6\ \ 7\ \ 8\ \ 9\ \ 10}{\vert\vert\vert\vert\vert\vert\vert\vert\vert\vert\vert\vert\vert\vert\vert\vert\vert\vert\vert\vert\vert}$$

2. $3 - 4 + 6$	**6.** $5 - 3 + 9$	**10.** $5 - 9 + 3$
3. $2 + 6 - 4$	**7.** $3 - 2 + 1$	**11.** $6 + 5 - 4$
4. $-3 + 2 - 4$	**8.** $-7 + 9 - 2$	**12.** $-3 - 7 + 9$
5. $-4 + 2 - 4$	**9.** $3 - 2 - 3$	**13.** $2 - 7 - 6$

14. $-3 - 5$	**17.** $5 - 9$	**20.** $6 - 7 - 2$
15. $-2 - 4 - 3$	**18.** $4 - 8 - 3$	**21.** $-1 - 8 + 7$
16. $6 - 3$	**19.** $2 - 5 + 3 - 6$	**22.** $-5 + 3 + 4 - 8$

USING A CALCULATOR WITH BRACKETS

When using a calculator with brackets it is possible to do calculations like those in Exercise 11 all in one calculation.

You need to be very careful to make sure that you do the operations in the right order and that you remember to close the brackets.

EXERCISE 1m

Calculate   a) $\frac{3 + 6}{3}$ b) $3 + \frac{6}{3}$

a) (We want to make sure that the addition is done first.)

$$\frac{3 + 6}{3} = \frac{(3 + 6)}{3}$$

(Press $\boxed{(}\ \boxed{3}\ \boxed{+}\ \boxed{6}\ \boxed{)}\ \boxed{\div}\ \boxed{3}\ \boxed{=}$)

$$= 3$$

b) (We want to make sure that the division is done first.)

$$3 + \frac{6}{3} = 3 + (6 \div 3)$$

(Press $\boxed{3}\ \boxed{+}\ \boxed{(}\ \boxed{6}\ \boxed{\div}\ \boxed{3}\ \boxed{)}\ \boxed{=}$)

$$= 5$$

In each question, put in any brackets that are needed to make sure that the operations are done in the right order. Then use your calculator to find the answer.

1. $\frac{4-1}{2}$

6. $6 \times 2 + 4 \div 2$

11. $8 + 2 \div (4 - 2)$

2. $(4 + 3) \times (4 - 1)$

7. $\frac{4}{5} + \frac{3}{2}$

12. $\frac{3+2}{3-1}$

3. $4 + 3 \times 4 - 1$

8. $8 + 2 \div 4 - 2$

13. $(8 + 2) \div (4 - 2)$

4. $4 - 1 \div 2$

9. $5 + \frac{2}{3-1}$

14. $6 + \frac{3}{3+3}$

5. $\frac{8+2}{4-2}$

10. $(8 + 2) \div 4 - 2$

15. $5 \div 2 + 3 \times 2$

MULTIPLICATION AND DIVISION BY POWERS OF TEN

When a number is multiplied by a power of 10, such as 100 or 1000 or 10 itself, the figures of the number move to the *left*.

When dividing, the figures move to the *right*.

EXERCISE 1n

Find   a) 72×100 b) 80×4000

a) $72 \times 100 = 7200$

b) $80 \times 4000 = 80 \times 4 \times 1000$
$$= 320 \times 1000$$
$$= 320\,000$$

Find

1. 81×1000

3. 600×200

5. 800×50

2. 1100×20

4. 70×700

6. 3200×30

Find   a) $3200 \div 10$ b) $36\,000 \div 600$

a) $3200 \div 10 = 320$

b) $36\,000 \div 600 = 360 \div 6$ (We divide by 100 first.)
$= 60$

Find

7. $7000 \div 100$ **9.** $3600 \div 60$ **11.** $48\,000 \div 40$

8. $240 \div 20$ **10.** $48\,000 \div 4000$ **12.** $6000 \div 50$

13. Cup-hooks come in boxes of 40. How many hooks are there in 30 boxes?

14. In a warehouse, each shelf holds 400 tins of soup. There are 50 shelves. How many tins can the shelves hold altogether?

15. Hiji television sets sell for £300 each. A store takes £9000 from sales of these sets. How many are sold?

16. A machine cuts a roll of paper into separate sheets of wrapping paper each 60 cm long. If 200 sheets can be cut from the roll, how long is the paper in the roll?

17. If 60 pages contain 12 000 words, how many words on average are there on each page?

18. A market gardener plants 8000 lettuces in 40 equal rows. How many plants are there per row?

19. Textbooks were delivered to a school in boxes of 40. If 200 textbooks were ordered, how many boxes were sent?

20. A certain magazine contains 80 pages. How many pages are there in 200 of these magazines?

LONG MULTIPLICATION ━━━━━━━━━━━━━━━━━━━━━━━━━━━

EXERCISE 1p

Find 231×34

$$\begin{array}{r} 231 \\ \times \quad 34 \\ \hline 924 \\ 6930 \\ \hline 7854 \\ \hline \end{array}$$

(First multiply by 4.)
(Now multiply by 30.)
(Then add the results.)

(Rough check: $200 \times 30 = 6000$.   This is the same sort of size as 7854.)

$231 \times 34 = 7854$

Find

1. 46×35

2. 78×17

3. 134×24

4. 245×36

5. 123×23

6. 178×29

7. 215×31

8. 62×19

9. 244×52

10. Each box of Sweet Delight chocolates contains 42 chocolates. How many chocolates are there in 24 boxes?

11. A firm exports tins of fruit in cartons. Each lorry container holds 206 cartons.
a) How many cartons are there in 13 containers?
b) Each carton holds 32 tins. How many tins are there in one container?

12. A rectangular hall is to be carpeted with carpet tiles. 16 tiles are needed one way and 24 the other.
How many tiles are needed if there are to be 5 spare tiles?

13. Pupils each pay 82 p for their lunch. How much money is collected from 24 pupils?

14. Chairs for the school canteen cost £19 each. What is the cost of buying 182 chairs?

15. Each flat owner in a block pays £42 a quarter to the maintenance fund. There are 18 flats. How much goes into the fund each quarter?

16. Making a miniature chair takes 57 minutes. In minutes, how long does it take to make 17 such chairs?

17. The Parks Department of a town ordered 16 bags of mixed daffodil bulbs. Each bag cost £4.50.
What was the total cost of the bulbs in
a) pence   b) pounds?

18. A florist bought 75 pots of polyanthus plants for a total of £48.
a) He sold all but three pots at 92 p each. How much money did he take?
b) How much profit did he make on the pots?

DIVISION

EXERCISE 1q

Find   a) $84 \div 6$ b) $184 \div 9$

a) $\begin{array}{r} 1\,4 \\ 6\overline{)8\,^24} \end{array}$ b) $\begin{array}{r} 2\,0 \quad \text{remainder } 4 \\ 9\overline{)1\,8\,4} \end{array}$

   $84 \div 6 = 14$ $184 \div 9 = 20$, remainder 4

In each case, find the answer, giving the remainder if there is one.

1. $110 \div 7$ **4.** $73 \div 3$ **7.** $183 \div 8$

2. $92 \div 5$ **5.** $124 \div 9$ **8.** $95 \div 6$

3. $97 \div 4$ **6.** $100 \div 7$ **9.** $248 \div 4$

10. $194 \div 3$ **13.** $164 \div 9$ **16.** $99 \div 8$

11. $78 \div 6$ **14.** $182 \div 7$ **17.** $61 \div 2$

12. $202 \div 2$ **15.** $341 \div 5$ **18.** $61 \div 3$

19. In an examination hall there are 121 desks laid out 9 to a row. How many complete rows are there and how many desks are there in the last, incomplete, row?

20. A flower seller buys 216 freesias and makes them up into bunches each containing 8 flowers. How many bunches are there?

21. Joe packs 172 eggs into containers each holding half a dozen. How many containers will he fill and how many eggs will be left over?

22. Stuart, Mary, Sue and Isabel share £147 equally. They each take the largest possible whole number of pounds and what is left goes to charity.
How much goes to charity?

23. A batch of 1350 matches is to be packed into 7 boxes, each containing the same number of matches.
How many will there be in each box and how many matches will be left over?

LONG DIVISION

EXERCISE 1r

Find $714 \div 21$

$$
\begin{array}{r}
34 \\
21 \overline{)714} \\
63 \\
\overline{84} \\
84 \\
\overline{0}
\end{array}
$$

$21 \times 2 = 42, \quad 21 \times 3 = 63$

$21 \times 4 = 84$

(Rough check: $700 \div 20 = 70 \div 2 = 35$)

$714 \div 21 = 34$

Find

1.	492 ÷ 41	**4.**	608 ÷ 19	**7.**	285 ÷ 15
2.	408 ÷ 17	**5.**	704 ÷ 32	**8.**	464 ÷ 16
3.	900 ÷ 25	**6.**	396 ÷ 22	**9.**	456 ÷ 24

10.	837 ÷ 31	**12.**	364 ÷ 14	**14.**	810 ÷ 18
11.	504 ÷ 42	**13.**	693 ÷ 33	**15.**	714 ÷ 21

16. How many days do 408 hours make?

17. A ship takes an hour to sail 27 km. How long will it take to travel 378 km?

18. Sheila knits a scarf with 1008 rows. There are 14 rows to the inch. How long is the scarf in inches?

19. A pile of text books is 42 cm high.
   a) Give 42 cm in mm.
   b) Each book is 14 mm thick. How many books are there in the pile?

20. The floor of a room 7 m wide is to be covered with tiles 12 cm square.
   a) How many complete tiles will fit across the room?
   b) How much space is there still to fill across the room?

MIXED EXERCISES

EXERCISE 1s **1.** From the set {1, 2, 5, 9, 12, 18, 21, 36, 39, 41} write down the numbers that are
   a) prime   d) multiples of 2
   b) odd   e) multiples of 3
   c) even   f) factors of 36.

2. Find the highest number that is a factor of
   a) both 6 and 4   b) both 15 and 20   c) both 8 and 20.

3. Find the lowest number that is a multiple of
   a) both 2 and 3   b) both 4 and 5   c) both 3 and 6.

4. Calculate
  a) $2 \times 4 + 3$ b) $2 + 4 \times 3$ c) $2 \times (4 + 3)$

5. Calculate
  a) 45×23 b) $219 \div 24$ and give the remainder.

EXERCISE 1t **1.** From the set $\{4, 5, 6, 8, 12, 15, 20, 21, 23, 27, 29\}$ write down the numbers that are
  a) odd   d) prime
  b) multiples of 5   e) even
  c) factors of 40   f) multiples of 4.

2. Calculate
  a) $16 \times 2 \times 4$ b) $16 \times 2 - 4$ c) $16 - 2 \times 4$

3. Find $172 \div 9$ and give the remainder.

4. Find a) 112×34 b) $345 \div 15$

5. Find the difference between the place values of the 3 and the 4 in 3124.

EXERCISE 1u In this exercise you have several alternative answers. Write down the letter that corresponds to the correct answer.

1. The prime numbers in the set $\{1, 2, 4, 7, 11, 15\}$ are
  A 1, 2, 7, 11   **B** 2, 4   **C** 2, 7, 11   **D** 2, 7, 11, 15

2. The value of $2 + 3 \times 2$ is
  A 7   **B** 10   **C** 6   **D** 8

3. The square numbers in the set $\{2, 4, 8, 9, 10, 16, 20\}$ are
  A 4, 9, 16   **B** 4, 8, 10, 16, 20   **C** 2, 4, 8, 9, 16

4. The highest number that is a factor of both 6 and 8 is
  A 2   **B** 4   **C** 1   **D** 24

5. The value of $3000 - 3$ is
  A 2007   **B** 2997   **C** 2907   **D** 2700

2 PATTERNS AND SEQUENCES

GEOMETRIC PATTERNS

EXERCISE 2a Copy each pattern onto 5 mm squared or dotted paper and continue
the pattern to the edge of the page.

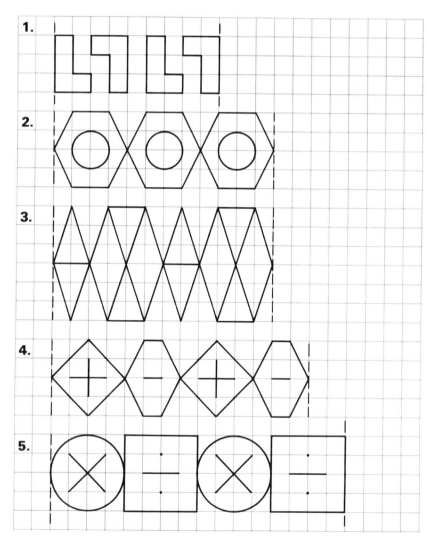

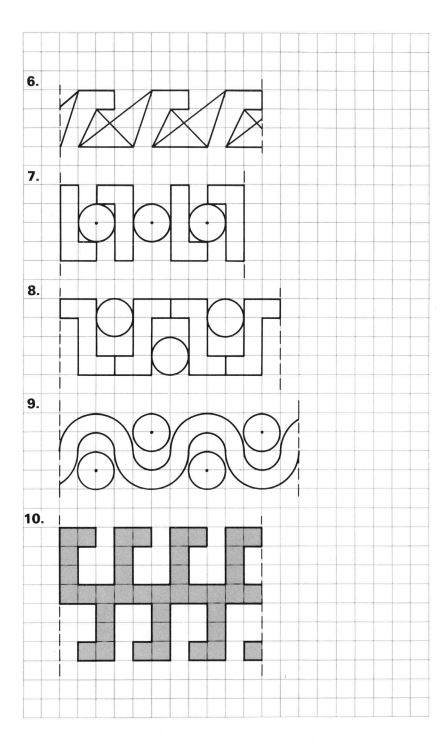

6.

7.

8.

9.

10.

CHANGING PATTERNS

The patterns in Exercise 2a remain the same as we continue to draw them. Those in the next exercise change.

EXERCISE 2b Use 5 mm squared or dotted paper to draw the next two arrangements for each of the following patterns.

Allow yourself plenty of space for each question.

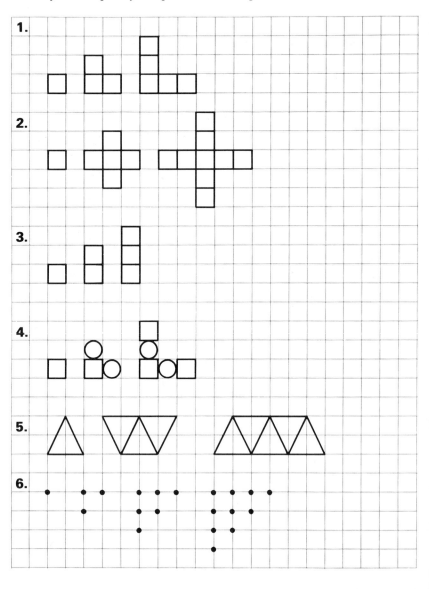

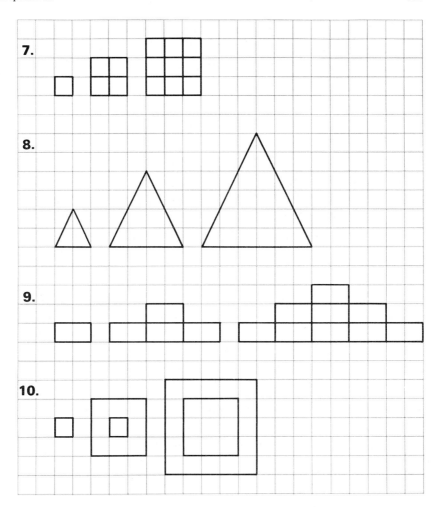

SEQUENCES

The numbers of squares required to make the pattern in question 1 of Exercise 2b are   1, 3, 5, 7, 9   and so on. Each new number is obtained by adding 2 to the number immediately in front of it. This is an example of a *sequence*.

A list of numbers which has a pattern that can be used to continue the list is called a sequence.

1, 4, 9, 16, 25, ...   is also a sequence. The rule here is to square the consecutive whole numbers   1, 2, 3, 4, 5, ...

EXERCISE 2c

Start with 3 and write down the next four terms in the sequence you get by adding 4 each time.

The sequence is 3, 7, 11, 15, 19, ...

In each question from 1 to 8 write down the first five terms in the sequence you get by carrying out the instructions.

1. Start with 2 and add 3 each time.

2. Start with 5 and add 5 each time.

3. Start with the terms 1, 2, ...   Each new term is found by adding together the two terms in front of it.

4. Start with 50 and take away 3 each time.

5. Start with 100 and take away 10 each time.

6. Start with 3 and double the number each time.

7. Start with 1 and treble the number each time.

8. Start with 20 and subtract 2 each time.

For each of the following sequences write down the next two numbers.

9. 3, 6, 9, 12, ...

10. 5, 9, 13, 17, ...

11. 4, 8, 16, 32, ...

12. 5, 8, 12, 17, ...

13. 64, 32, 16, 8, ...

14. 4, 5, 7, 10, ...

For each of the following sequences describe what is done to each number to get the number that follows it. Give the next two numbers in each sequence.

15. 4, 9, 14, 19, ...

16. 3, 8, 13, 18, ...

17. 5, 10, 20, 40, ...

18. 60, 56, 52, 48, ...

SPECIAL NUMBERS

In Book 2B we saw that 1, 4, 9, 16, ... were called square numbers. They are the numbers of dots required to make larger and larger squares, as we can see below.

Similarly, we saw that 1, 3, 6, 10, ... were triangular numbers.

If a number of dots, 6 for example, can be arranged to form a complete rectangle like this ⋮⋮⋮ the number is called a rectangular number. We cannot make a rectangle using exactly 7 dots, so 7 is not a rectangular number.

EXERCISE 2d

1. Write down the first eight square numbers.

2. Write down the first eight triangular numbers.

3. Determine whether or not each of the following numbers is a rectangular number. Draw all the possible rectangles for each rectangular number.
5, 6, 12, 15, 16, 20, 24.
(Note that square numbers are also rectangular numbers because a square is a special type of rectangle.)

4. Write down the first six rectangular numbers.

5. The numbers 3, 5 and 7 are not rectangular. Write down the next three non-rectangular numbers. These numbers belong to a special group of numbers. What is the name of this group of numbers?

6. Consider the square numbers 1, 4, 9, 16, 25, ...
If we work out

"2nd term − 1st term", "3rd term − 2nd term", ...

i.e.   4 − 1,   9 − 4,   ...

we get a set of numbers called the *first differences*.

We can do the same with the first differences and get a set of numbers called the *second differences*.

a) Copy this pattern and complete it.

	1st		2nd		3rd		4th		5th		6th		7th		8th	
Square numbers	1		4		9											
First differences		3		5		7										
Second differences			2		2											

b) Do the first differences form a sequence? Comment on the pattern you get.

c) Do the second differences form a sequence? Comment on the pattern you get.

7. a) Write down the next four terms in the sequence
            1, 2, 4, 8, ...

b) Copy this pattern and complete it.

	1st		2nd		3rd		4th		5th		6th		7th		8th	
Sequence	1		2		4		8									
First differences																
Second differences																

(First and second differences are defined in question 6.)

c) Do the first differences form a sequence? Comment on the pattern you get.

d) Do the second differences form a sequence? Comment on the pattern you get.

8. Repeat question 6 starting with the triangular numbers.

9.

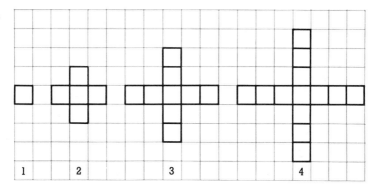

a) Count the number of squares needed to make each of these shapes. Copy the table and enter your results in it.

Diagram number	1	2	3	4
No. of squares				

b) Without drawing a diagram, can you say how many squares would be needed to draw diagram number 5 and to draw diagram number 6?

c) Write down the number missing from the following sentence.
The number of extra squares needed each time to make the next diagram is ___ .

10.

a) Draw the next two diagrams in this pattern.

b) Count the number of matchsticks required to make each of these shapes.

c) Copy the table and enter your results in it.

Diagram number	1	2	3	4	5
Number of matchsticks					

d) Without drawing a diagram, can you say how many matchsticks are needed for diagram number 6?

11. The first six terms of a sequence are 9, 32, 75, 144, 245, 384.
We want to find the next two terms.

    a) There is no obvious pattern in this sequence. Copy and complete this table.

Sequence	9		32		75		144		245		384				
First difference															
Second difference															
Third difference															

    b) What is the pattern in the third differences?
    c) Use this pattern to continue the second differences.
    d) Now continue the first differences.
    e) Now find the next two terms in the sequence.

12. Repeat question 11 for the sequence whose first six terms are 6, 24, 60, 120, 210, 336.

3 FRACTIONS AND DECIMALS

FRACTIONS

EXERCISE 3a Write down the fraction of the figure that is shaded.

1.

6.

2.

7.

3.

8.

4.

9.

5.

10.

11. Copy the diagram on to squared paper and then shade $\frac{2}{3}$ of it. How many twelfths of your figure is this?

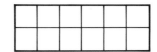

27

12. Copy the diagram on to squared paper and shade $\frac{1}{3}$ of it. How many fifteenths of your figure is this?

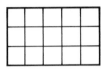

13. Make two copies of this diagram.

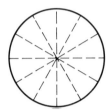

a) Shade $\frac{5}{12}$ of the diagram.

b) Shade $\frac{2}{3}$ of the diagram.

14. Trace this diagram and shade $\frac{1}{2}$ of it.

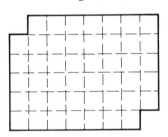

FINDING FRACTIONS OF QUANTITIES

The school gave $\frac{2}{5}$ of the money raised at a summer fair to a local charity.

To find the amount given to the charity, we can first find $\frac{1}{5}$ of £4500.

$$\frac{1}{5} \text{ of } £4500 = £4500 \div 5$$
$$= £900$$

Then to find $\frac{2}{5}$ of £4500, we multiply £900 by 2

i.e. $\frac{2}{5}$ of £4500 $=$ £900 $\times$ 2

                                            $=$ £1800

As we have to both divide by 5 and multiply by 2, we could choose to multiply first,

i.e. $\frac{2}{5}$ of £4500 $=$ £$(2 \times 4500) \div 5$

                                            $=$ £9000 $\div$ 5

                                            $=$ £1800

EXERCISE 3b

Find $\frac{3}{4}$ of 96 m

($\frac{3}{4}$ of 96 m is 96 m divided by 4 and multiplied by 3.)

$\frac{3}{4}$ of 96 m $=$ $(96 \div 4) \times 3$ m

            $=$ 24 $\times$ 3 m

            $=$ 72 m

Find

1. $\frac{1}{5}$ of £80   **5.** $\frac{1}{6}$ of £90   **9.** $\frac{1}{4}$ of £120

2. $\frac{2}{3}$ of £18   **6.** $\frac{3}{8}$ of 112 m   **10.** $\frac{2}{5}$ of 350 cm

3. $\frac{3}{4}$ of 84 cm   **7.** $\frac{4}{9}$ of £1206   **11.** $\frac{4}{7}$ of £168

4. $\frac{3}{5}$ of 75 kg   **8.** $\frac{3}{7}$ of 672 g   **12.** $\frac{5}{8}$ of 424 kg

13.   Winston bought 36 m of tape and gave $\frac{2}{9}$ of it to his sister.
           a) What length of tape did Winston give to his sister?
           b) What length of tape did Winston keep?

14. The P.T.A. raised £1080 at a car boot sale.

    a) One tenth of the sum raised went on expenses. What did the expenses amount to?

    b) The school was given $\frac{4}{5}$ of the sum raised. How much did the school receive?

    c) The P.T.A. kept the rest of the money. How much did they keep?

15.

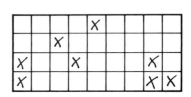

This is a patio made from square paving stones. The stones with a cross on them are cracked. John had a quick look and said "A quarter of the stones are cracked".

    a) How many stones are there in the patio altogether?

    b) What fraction of the stones are actually cracked?

    c) Did John overestimate or underestimate the number of cracked stones and by how many?

EQUIVALENT FRACTIONS

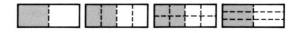

These diagrams show that $\frac{1}{2}, \frac{2}{4}, \frac{4}{8}$ and $\frac{3}{6}$ are *equivalent fractions*.

We can find fractions equivalent to a given fraction by multiplying the top *and* the bottom by the same number,

e.g.
$$\frac{1}{2} = \frac{1 \times 5}{2 \times 5} = \frac{5}{10}$$

and
$$\frac{3}{4} = \frac{3 \times 2}{4 \times 2} = \frac{6}{8}$$

EXERCISE 3c

Find the missing number to make $\frac{10}{}$ equivalent to $\frac{2}{3}$.

$$\frac{2}{3} = \frac{10}{}$$

(If $\frac{2}{3} = \frac{10}{}$ the top has been multiplied by 5.)

Therefore $\qquad\qquad \frac{2}{3} = \frac{2 \times 5}{3 \times 5} = \frac{10}{15}$

Fill in the missing number to make the fractions equivalent.

1. $\frac{1}{4} = \frac{}{8}$

2. $\frac{3}{4} = \frac{}{12}$

3. $\frac{1}{8} = \frac{2}{}$

4. $\frac{2}{3} = \frac{8}{}$

5. $\frac{2}{5} = \frac{}{10}$

6. $\frac{1}{3} = \frac{}{9}$

7. $\frac{3}{5} = \frac{9}{}$

8. $\frac{3}{7} = \frac{6}{}$

9. $\frac{5}{9} = \frac{}{27}$

10. $\frac{3}{8} = \frac{}{32}$

11. Express $\frac{2}{3}$ as ninths.

12. Express $\frac{3}{4}$ as sixteenths.

13. Express $\frac{3}{10}$ as thirtieths.

14. Express $\frac{1}{12}$ as thirtysixths.

15. Express $\frac{4}{5}$ as twentieths.

16. Express $\frac{5}{8}$ as twentyfourths.

17. Give three fractions that are equivalent to $\frac{2}{5}$

18. Give three fractions that are equivalent to $\frac{1}{2}$

THIS MEANS WRITE $\frac{2}{3}$ AS $\frac{}{9}$.

SIMPLIFYING FRACTIONS

We know that $\qquad \frac{2}{4} = \frac{1}{2}$

When we write $\frac{2}{4}$ as $\frac{1}{2}$ we have *simplified* $\frac{2}{4}$

When the top and bottom of a fraction have a common factor, we can simplify the fraction if we divide both top and bottom by that common factor. (This is called cancelling.)

Consider the fraction $\frac{9}{15}$

The numbers 9 and 15 have a common factor of 3.

Dividing each by 3 gives $\quad \dfrac{\cancel{9}^{3}}{\cancel{15}_{5}} = \dfrac{3}{5}$

The numbers 3 and 5 do not have any common factors so we cannot simplify the fraction any further.

When this is the case we say that the fraction is expressed in its *lowest terms* or in its simplest form.

EXERCISE 3d

> Simplify $\frac{15}{45}$ as far as possible.
>
> $$\dfrac{\cancel{15}^{\cancel{3}^{1}}}{\cancel{45}_{\cancel{9}_{3}}} = \dfrac{1}{3}$$

Simplify as far as possible

1. $\frac{6}{9}$	**5.** $\frac{15}{30}$	**9.** $\frac{8}{12}$	**13.** $\frac{8}{10}$
2. $\frac{4}{8}$	**6.** $\frac{6}{18}$	**10.** $\frac{6}{8}$	**14.** $\frac{9}{15}$
3. $\frac{3}{15}$	**7.** $\frac{2}{8}$	**11.** $\frac{5}{20}$	**15.** $\frac{10}{18}$
4. $\frac{4}{12}$	**8.** $\frac{15}{20}$	**12.** $\frac{9}{12}$	**16.** $\frac{14}{21}$

NUMERATORS AND DENOMINATORS

The top number of a fraction is called the *numerator*.

The bottom number of a fraction is called the *denominator*.

It is the denominator of a fraction that tells us whether the fraction is "halves" or "thirds" or "quarters" and so on.

ADDING AND SUBTRACTING FRACTIONS

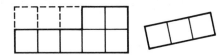

We have removed $\frac{3}{10}$ of the diagram.

Another $\frac{1}{10}$ of the diagram has been taken away, and now $\frac{4}{10}$ have been removed altogether.

i.e.
$$\frac{3}{10} + \frac{1}{10} = \frac{4}{10}$$

We add $\frac{3}{10}$ and $\frac{1}{10}$ by adding the numerators, and we can do this because $\frac{3}{10}$ and $\frac{1}{10}$ are both "tenths".

We can add or subtract fractions when they have the same *denominator*.

We do this by adding or subtracting the *numerators*.

EXERCISE 3e

Find $\frac{3}{7} - \frac{2}{7}$

$$\frac{3}{7} - \frac{2}{7} = \frac{3-2}{7}$$
$$= \frac{1}{7}$$

Find

1. $\frac{1}{5} + \frac{3}{5}$

2. $\frac{1}{7} + \frac{2}{7}$

3. $\frac{4}{11} - \frac{3}{11}$

4. $\frac{5}{9} - \frac{1}{9}$

5. $\frac{4}{5} - \frac{2}{5}$

6. $\frac{2}{5} + \frac{2}{5}$

7. $\frac{6}{13} + \frac{5}{13}$

8. $\frac{9}{10} - \frac{6}{10}$

9. $\frac{4}{9} + \frac{3}{9}$

Add $\frac{9}{22}$ and $\frac{5}{22}$ and simplify the answer.

$$\frac{9}{22} + \frac{5}{22} = \frac{\cancel{14}^{7}}{\cancel{22}_{11}}$$

$$= \frac{7}{11}$$

Add or subtract the fractions and simplify the answer.

10. $\frac{1}{8} + \frac{3}{8}$ **15.** $\frac{1}{15} + \frac{2}{15}$ **20.** $\frac{5}{8} - \frac{3}{8}$

11. $\frac{3}{10} - \frac{1}{10}$ **16.** $\frac{5}{9} - \frac{2}{9}$ **21.** $\frac{5}{9} + \frac{4}{9}$

12. $\frac{13}{20} - \frac{7}{20}$ **17.** $\frac{1}{12} + \frac{5}{12}$ **22.** $\frac{5}{16} - \frac{1}{16}$

13. $\frac{3}{4} - \frac{1}{4}$ **18.** $\frac{2}{5} + \frac{3}{5}$ **23.** $\frac{5}{12} - \frac{3}{12}$

14. $\frac{2}{9} + \frac{1}{9}$ **19.** $\frac{4}{7} + \frac{3}{7}$ **24.** $\frac{7}{12} + \frac{5}{12}$

25.

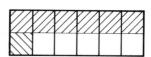

a) What fraction of the diagram is shaded like this ?

b) What fraction of the diagram is shaded like this ⬚ ?

c) Count all the shaded squares and write down the shaded fraction of the diagram.

d) Hence write down the sum of the fractions given by your answers to parts (a) and (b).

26.

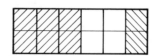

a) What fraction of the diagram is shaded like this ?

b) What fraction of the diagram is shaded like this ?

c) What is the sum of these two fractions?

27.

Copy this diagram on to squared paper.

a) Shade $\frac{1}{3}$ of the diagram.

b) Use a different colour to shade $\frac{1}{6}$ of the diagram.

c) What fraction of the diagram have you shaded in total?

28.

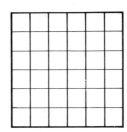

Make a separate copy of the diagram for each part of this question.

a) Use one copy to find $\frac{1}{4} + \frac{1}{3}$.

b) Use another copy to find $\frac{1}{9} + \frac{3}{4}$.

c) Use the third copy to find $\frac{5}{6} - \frac{2}{9}$.

MIXED NUMBERS AND IMPROPER FRACTIONS

A mixed number is the sum of a whole number and a fraction. For example "one and a half" means $1 + \frac{1}{2}$ and is written as $1\frac{1}{2}$.

Now $1 = \frac{2}{2}$ so $1\frac{1}{2} = \frac{2}{2} + \frac{1}{2} = \frac{3}{2}$

$\frac{3}{2}$ is called an improper fraction.

Whenever the numerator of a fraction is bigger than its denominator it is called an *improper fraction*.

To change an improper fraction into a mixed number, we divide the numerator by the denominator to give the number of units. The remainder is the number of fractional parts.

For example $\qquad\qquad\qquad \frac{17}{5} = 3\frac{2}{5}$

To change a mixed number into an improper fraction, we multiply the units by the denominator and then add the result to the numerator.

For example $\qquad 4\frac{1}{3} = \frac{12}{3} + \frac{1}{3} = \frac{13}{3}$

EXERCISE 3f Change the following improper fractions to mixed numbers.

1. $\frac{5}{2}$	**4.** $\frac{7}{4}$	**7.** $\frac{5}{3}$	**10.** $\frac{11}{5}$
2. $\frac{4}{3}$	**5.** $\frac{9}{5}$	**8.** $\frac{7}{2}$	**11.** $\frac{9}{8}$
3. $\frac{7}{3}$	**6.** $\frac{15}{7}$	**9.** $\frac{9}{4}$	**12.** $\frac{17}{3}$

Change the following mixed numbers to improper fractions.

13. $1\frac{2}{3}$	**16.** $1\frac{2}{5}$	**19.** $1\frac{1}{3}$	**22.** $3\frac{2}{7}$
14. $2\frac{1}{2}$	**17.** $3\frac{1}{3}$	**20.** $2\frac{1}{5}$	**23.** $4\frac{1}{4}$
15. $1\frac{3}{4}$	**18.** $2\frac{1}{4}$	**21.** $1\frac{1}{4}$	**24.** $3\frac{3}{4}$

DECIMALS

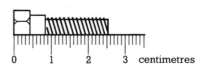

Using fractions we can write the length of this bolt as about $2\frac{1}{2}$ cm or as $2\frac{5}{10}$ cm.

In decimal notation we write its length as 2.5 cm.

If we could see hundredths and thousandths of a centimetre we could write the length as 2.524 cm.

The point is called the decimal point.

The first figure to the right of the point means "tenths" and its position is called the first decimal place.

The second figure to the right of the point means "hundredths" and its position is called the second decimal place.

The third figure to the right of the point means "thousandths" and its position is called the third decimal place, and so on.

EXERCISE 3g

Write these numbers in order with the smallest number first.

$$1.035, \ 0.89, \ 5.1, \ 0.802$$

1.035, 0.890, 5.100, 0.802

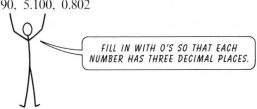

FILL IN WITH 0'S SO THAT EACH NUMBER HAS THREE DECIMAL PLACES.

(Look at the units first, then the tenths and so on.)

0.802, 0.89, 1.035, 5.1

1. What is the value of the figure 3 in each of the following numbers?

   a) 32.19   b) 4.032   c) 13.006   d) 0.883   e) 7.3

2. From the list   2.05, 6.19, 4.335, 2.009   write down

   a) the largest number   b) the smallest number.

3. Write these numbers in order of size with the largest first:

$$20, \ 0.22, \ 2.8, \ 0.022$$

4. Write down the figure in the second decimal place in the number 2.747

5. Write one and seven tenths as a decimal number.

6. Write one and seven hundredths as a decimal number.

7. Which of these numbers are the same?

$$45.7, \ 4.57, \ 7.045, \ 4.057, \ 4.570$$

8. Write the number twenty four hundredths in decimal notation.

9. Write each of the following numbers as a fraction in its simplest form

   a) 0.5   b) 0.25   c) 0.05   d) 0.005

ADDITION AND SUBTRACTION OF DECIMALS

Decimals are added and subtracted in the same way as whole numbers. It is sensible to write them in a column so that the decimal points are in a vertical line. This makes sure that units are added to units, tenths are added to tenths and so on.

It is also sometimes necessary to use noughts after the decimal points so that both numbers have the same number of decimal places.

For example, $3 - 0.82$ can be written as

$$\begin{array}{r} 3.00 \\ -0.82 \\ \hline \end{array}$$

EXERCISE 3h

Find $1.5 - 0.92$

$1.5 - 0.92 = 0.58$

$$\begin{array}{r} 1.50 \\ -0.92 \\ \hline 0.58 \\ \hline \end{array}$$

Find

1. $1.2 + 0.7$	**4.** $1.3 - 0.16$	**7.** $2.1 - 0.8$
2. $1.2 - 0.7$	**5.** $0.73 - 0.002$	**8.** $3.5 + 1.2$
3. $3.6 + 0.8$	**6.** $1.7 - 0.08$	**9.** $1.5 - 0.47$
10. $18.04 - 12$	**13.** $26.56 + 1.24$	**16.** $24.5 - 8$
11. $5 + 0.17$	**14.** $17 - 1.92$	**17.** $6 - 5.73$
12. $8 - 1.25$	**15.** $25 - 10.6$	**18.** $3 - 0.72$

INTERCHANGING DECIMALS AND FRACTIONS ⎯⎯⎯⎯⎯⎯

EXERCISE 3i

Express 0.12 as a fraction.

$$0.12 = \frac{1}{10} + \frac{2}{100}$$

$$= \frac{10}{100} + \frac{2}{100}$$

$$= \frac{\cancel{12}^{3}}{\cancel{100}_{25}}$$

$$= \frac{3}{25}$$

Express the following decimals as fractions in their simplest form.

1.	0.5	**5.**	0.03	**9.**	0.002	**13.**	0.7
2.	0.04	**6.**	1.35	**10.**	0.008	**14.**	0.05
3.	0.8	**7.**	0.125	**11.**	0.75	**15.**	0.25
4.	0.15	**8.**	1.25	**12.**	3.75	**16.**	0.005

Express $\frac{3}{4}$ as a decimal.

(Remember that $\frac{3}{4} = 3 \div 4$)

$$\frac{3}{4} = 0.75 \qquad\qquad \begin{array}{r} 0.75 \\ 4\overline{)3.0^20} \end{array}$$

Express the following fractions as decimals.

17.	$\frac{1}{2}$	**21.**	$\frac{3}{8}$	**25.**	$3\frac{1}{8}$	**29.**	$\frac{3}{5}$
18.	$\frac{1}{4}$	**22.**	$\frac{3}{100}$	**26.**	$1\frac{3}{4}$	**30.**	$\frac{3}{25}$
19.	$\frac{2}{5}$	**23.**	$2\frac{1}{2}$	**27.**	$\frac{7}{50}$	**31.**	$\frac{27}{100}$
20.	$\frac{7}{10}$	**24.**	$1\frac{1}{4}$	**28.**	$\frac{5}{8}$	**32.**	$2\frac{3}{4}$

Copy and complete the following table.

	Fraction	Decimal
33.	$\frac{4}{5}$	
34.		0.25
35.	$\frac{3}{4}$	
36.		0.5
37.	$1\frac{9}{10}$	
38.		0.125

39. Express as a decimal

a) $\frac{7}{8}$ b) $1\frac{3}{10}$ c) $\frac{7}{25}$

MULTIPLICATION AND DIVISION BY 10, 100, 1000

Remember that to multiply a number by 10, 100 or 1000 we move the figures one, two or three places to the *left*.

Remember that division is the opposite of multiplication, so to divide a number by 10, 100 or 1000 we move the figures one, two or three places to the *right*.

EXERCISE 3j

Find a) 4.078×100 c) 4.2×1000

b) $21.8 \div 100$ d) $0.3 \div 10$

a) $4.078 \times 100 = 407.8$

b) $21.8 \div 100 = 0.218$ (Notice that 0 is put before the point.)

c) $4.2 \times 1000 = 4200$

> WE NEED TO ADD 0'S TO FILL THE EMPTY COLUMNS.

d) $0.3 \div 10 = 0.03$

Find, without using a calculator,

1.	4.8×10	**8.**	$31.6 \div 100$	**15.**	0.52×1000
2.	$4.8 \div 10$	**9.**	$25 \div 10$	**16.**	$1.7 \div 10$
3.	0.34×10	**10.**	1.005×1000	**17.**	2.4×100
4.	$0.55 \div 10$	**11.**	7.31×10	**18.**	$0.02 \div 100$
5.	12.5×100	**12.**	0.52×100	**19.**	0.4×1000
6.	$9.74 \div 100$	**13.**	$7.8 \div 100$	**20.**	$5.52 \div 10$
7.	0.087×1000	**14.**	$0.4 \div 100$	**21.**	0.032×100

USING A CALCULATOR FOR MULTIPLICATION AND DIVISION

Remember that a number

increases when multiplied by a number *greater than one*
and *decreases* when multiplied by a number *less than one*

and that the *opposite* is true of division.

These facts will help you decide if an answer is reasonable.

EXERCISE 3k

Find $15.8 \div 0.4$

$15.8 \div 0.4 = 39.5$ (Press $\boxed{1}$ $\boxed{5}$ $\boxed{\cdot}$ $\boxed{8}$ $\boxed{\div}$ $\boxed{0}$ $\boxed{\cdot}$ $\boxed{4}$ $\boxed{=}$)

THIS IS REASONABLE, AS DIVISION
BY 0.4 MAKES 15.8 BIGGER.

Find

1.	16.3×4.3	**6.**	37.2×0.8	**11.**	0.18×0.27
2.	$3.9 \div 1.5$	**7.**	$4.7 \div 0.8$	**12.**	$0.56 \div 0.07$
3.	0.48×2.7	**8.**	35.2×1.6	**13.**	8.25×1.3
4.	$0.48 \div 1.2$	**9.**	$42.5 \div 0.17$	**14.**	52.6×26.3
5.	108×0.06	**10.**	$850 \div 3.4$	**15.**	$130 \div 5200$

16. Jason needed some sticky tape to seal bags of popcorn. Each bag needed about 0.02 m of tape and the roll of tape had 15 m on it. How many bags could be sealed with that roll of tape?

17. A rectangular floor measures 3.55 m by 1.8 m. What is its area?

18. How many wire nails, each 2.5 cm long, can be cut from a 4500 cm length of wire?

19. How many pieces, each 0.28 m long, can be cut from a 3.5 m length of wood?

20. A book is 1.8 cm thick. How many of these books can be stacked, one above the other, in a crate which is 1.17 m deep?

CORRECTING TO A GIVEN NUMBER OF DECIMAL PLACES

To correct a number to *one decimal place* we look at the figure in the *second decimal place*. If it is 5 or more we add 1 to the number in the first decimal place. If it is less than 5 we do not alter the number in the first decimal place.

For example $1.3 \vert 72 = 1.4$ correct to 1 d.p.

whereas $1.3 \vert 14 = 1.3$ correct to 1 d.p.

The same rule applies when correcting to any number of decimal places, i.e. always look at the next figure.

For example $1.372 \vert 8 = 1.373$ correct to 3 d.p.

It is sometimes unnecessary and often impossible to give decimal answers exactly. This is particularly true in the case of measurements. We do however need to know the degree of accuracy of an answer.

For example, if a manufacturer is asked to supply washers that are about $12\frac{1}{2}$ mm in diameter, he might think that 11 mm or $13\frac{1}{2}$ mm would be good enough.

If he has to make the diameter 12.5 mm correct to 1 decimal place then he knows what is acceptable and what is not.

Give 8.0473 correct to   a) 2 d.p.   b) 1 d.p.

a) 8.04 ¦ 73 = 8.05   to 2 d.p.
b) 8.0 ¦ 473 = 8.0   to 1 d.p.

(Notice that we leave the zero in the first d.p. to indicate that the number has been corrected to 1 d.p.)

EXERCISE 3I   Give the following numbers correct to 1 d.p.

1. 1.35	**3.** 0.17	**5.** 0.13	**7.** 2.373
2. 2.82	**4.** 0.08	**6.** 5.02	**8.** 5.105

Give the following numbers correct to 2 d.p.

9. 0.094	**11.** 0.125	**13.** 0.027	**15.** 52.373
10. 2.037	**12.** 10.104	**14.** 0.0053	**16.** 0.058

Give the following numbers correct to 3 d.p.

17. 8.1272	**20.** 0.0017	**23.** 0.000 92
18. 2.0335	**21.** 0.0235	**24.** 0.009 53
19. 4.6666	**22.** 0.1296	**25.** 1.0278

Give the following numbers correct to 4 d.p.

26. 0.012 733	**29.** 0.000 5326	**32.** 20.305 073
27. 2.469 912	**30.** 1.832 051	**33.** 1.008 020 8
28. 3.800 257	**31.** 10.882 56	**34.** 9.999 999 9

Give the following numbers correct to the number of decimal places indicated in brackets.

35. 82.1653 (2)	**38.** 0.012 76 (4)	**41.** 27.2939 (3)
36. 20.204 (1)	**39.** 1.3607 (3)	**42.** 0.006 914 (4)
37. 7.707 56 (3)	**40.** 15.821 (1)	**43.** 0.079 88 (3)

MORE FRACTIONS OF QUANTITIES

When we found fractions of quantities earlier in this chapter, the fractions were simple and the answers worked out exactly. Numbers are not usually this tidy in real life.

Consider this situation: there were 96 eggs in a crate and it was found that 23 of them were cracked. Therefore the fraction of the eggs that were cracked was $\frac{23}{96}$.

We want to illustrate this in a pie chart, so the "slice" of the circle representing the cracked eggs is $\frac{23}{96}$ of the whole circle. The angle we need to draw is $\frac{23}{96}$ of 360°.

To find $\frac{23}{96}$ of 360°, we need to divide by 96 and multiply by 23. It does not matter which we do first, but we will choose to do the multiplication before the division,

i.e. $\frac{23}{96}$ of 360°

$$= \frac{23}{96} \times 360°$$

$$= 23 \times 360° \div 96$$

(Press $\boxed{2}\,\boxed{3}\,\boxed{\times}\,\boxed{3}\,\boxed{6}\,\boxed{0}\,\boxed{\div}\,\boxed{9}\,\boxed{6}\,\boxed{=}$)

$$= 86.2\ldots°$$

$$= 86° \quad \text{to the nearest degree.}$$

EXERCISE 3m Use your calculator.

1. Find $\frac{3}{7}$ of £45 correct to the nearest penny.

2. Find   a) $\frac{34}{35}$ of 360°   b) $\frac{25}{44}$ of 360°   c) $\frac{13}{17}$ of 360°
giving each answer correct to the nearest degree.

3. Find $\frac{7}{9}$ of 86 m correct to the nearest tenth of a metre.

4. Find   a) $\frac{3}{13}$ of £60   b) $\frac{2}{17}$ of £25   c) $\frac{3}{16}$ of £82
giving each answer correct to the nearest penny.

5. Find   a) $\frac{12}{19}$ of 355 cm   b) $\frac{14}{23}$ of 290 cm   c) $\frac{1}{15}$ of 851 cm
giving each answer correct to the nearest centimetre.

6. Find   a) $\frac{7}{12}$ of 88 g   b) $\frac{13}{27}$ of 329 g   c) $\frac{122}{245}$ of 5800 g

giving each answer correct to the nearest gram.

7. Seventeen of the one hundred and twelve apples in a box were bad. The total weight of all the apples was seventeen kilograms. Find the weight of the bad apples. Decide yourself how accurate your answer should be. What might make your answer inaccurate ?

MIXED EXERCISES

EXERCISE 3n   **1.**   Find

a) $2.06 + 3.5$ b) $4.9 - 0.065$ c) 2.06×3.5 d) $2.06 \div 5$

2.   Express each decimal as a fraction in its simplest form.

a) 0.75   b) 0.04   c) 0.15   d) 0.105

3.   Express each fraction as a decimal correct to 3 decimal places.

a) $\frac{2}{7}$ b) $\frac{1}{15}$ c) $\frac{5}{9}$ d) $\frac{2}{3}$

4.   Express each fraction as a decimal correct to 3 decimal places and hence give these numbers in order of size with the smallest first.

$$1.58, \ 1\tfrac{2}{9}, \ 1.62, \ 1\tfrac{5}{7}$$

5.   a) Express $\frac{2}{5}$ as a decimal.

b) Use your answer to part (a) to find $\frac{2}{5}$ of £56.03 giving your answer correct to the nearest penny.

6.   Find the perimeter of this rectangle.

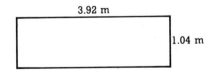

3.92 m

1.04 m

7.   Find $\frac{12}{29}$ of £85.50 giving your answer correct to the nearest penny.

8.   Find $\frac{4}{7} + \frac{6}{7}$ and give your answer as a mixed number.

9. On squared paper draw a rectangle 3 squares wide and 8 squares long.

a) Shade $\frac{3}{8}$ of your rectangle.

b) Shade $\frac{1}{3}$ of your rectangle.

c) Use your answers to (a) and (b) to find $\frac{3}{8} + \frac{1}{3}$.

10. Of the £350 raised at a school jumble sale, $\frac{2}{13}$ was given to charity.

Find, to the nearest penny, the amount given to charity.

EXERCISE 3p Do not use a calculator for this exercise.

1. Write $1\frac{2}{5}$ as an improper fraction.

6. Find $5.2 \div 100$

2. Find $\frac{2}{9} + \frac{4}{9}$

7. Give 0.022 59 to 3 d.p.

3. Find 2.7×100

8. Write $\frac{23}{9}$ as a mixed number.

4. Find $2.7 - 1.2$

9. Give $\frac{2}{3}$ as twelfths.

5. Find $\frac{3}{4}$ of 36 cm

10. Find $0.3 + 0.08$

EXERCISE 3q Each question is followed by several alternative ansers. Write down the letter that corresponds to the correct answer.

1. $2\frac{3}{5}$ can be written as

A $\frac{5}{5}$ **B** $\frac{8}{5}$ **C** $\frac{13}{5}$ **D** $\frac{3}{7}$

2. The value of $0.6 \div 10$ is

A 0.06   **B** 6   **C** 60   **D** 0.006

3. The value of 0.0098 correct to 2 d.p. is

A 0.00   **B** 0.01   **C** 0.10   **D** 0.0098

4. The value of $(0.4)^2$ is

A 0.44   **B** 1.6   **C** 0.8   **D** 0.16

5. The value of $\frac{2}{9} + \frac{3}{9}$ is

    A $\frac{5}{18}$ **B** $\frac{5}{9}$ **C** $\frac{6}{9}$ **D** $\frac{1}{9}$

6. The value of $0.2 + 0.05$ is

    A 0.7   **B** 0.07   **C** 2.5   **D** 0.25

4 REFLECTIONS AND ROTATIONS

REFLECTIONS

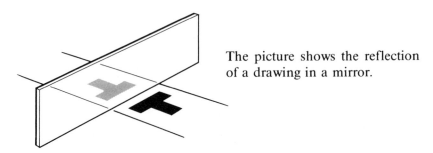

The picture shows the reflection of a drawing in a mirror.

If we imagine that the mirror is invisible we will just see the drawing and its image.

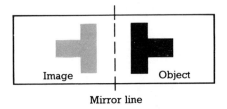

Image   Object

Mirror line

The object and its image are symmetrical, with the mirror line as the line of symmetry. If the paper is folded along the mirror line, the object fits exactly over the image.

EXERCISE 4a The dotted line is the mirror line. Copy the diagrams on to squared paper and draw the reflection of each object in the mirror line. Use a coloured pen to draw the image. Tracing paper may help you to position the image.

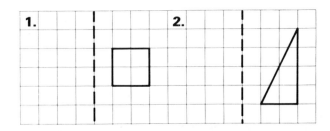

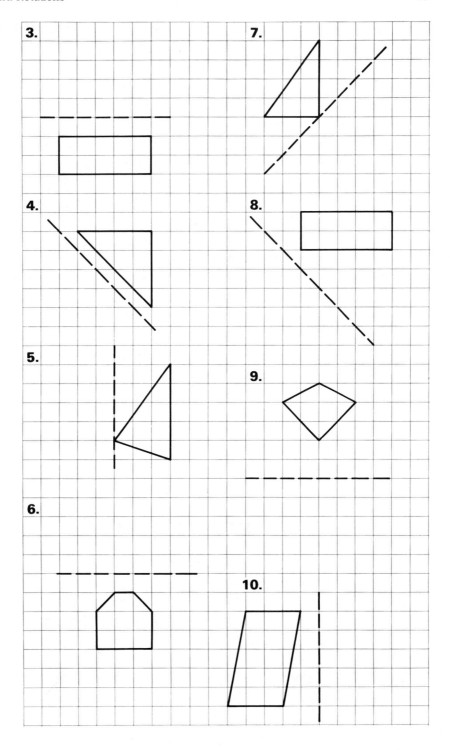

In the following diagrams the solid figure is the object and the dashed figure is the reflection. Copy these diagrams on to squared paper and draw the mirror line.

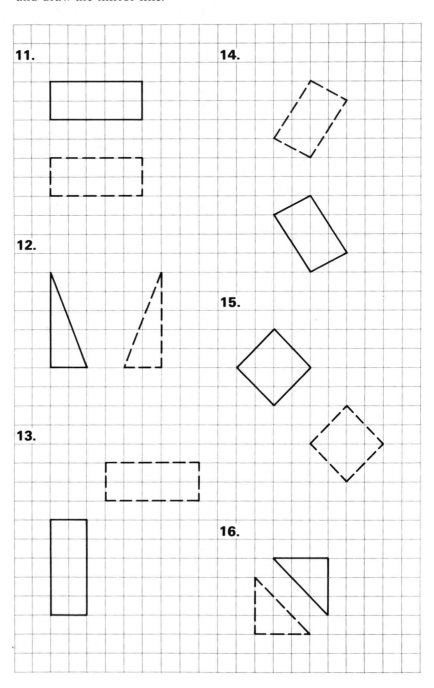

In each question from 17 to 20 copy the diagram on to squared paper and draw the reflection of the given shape

a) in the line AB. Mark it X.
b) in the line CD. Mark it Y.

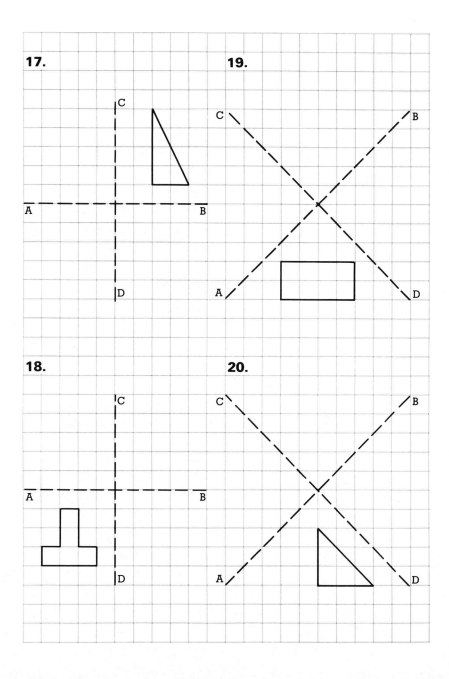

21. a) Draw the reflection of the given shape in the line AB. Mark it X.
    b) Draw the reflection of the given shape in the line CD. Mark it Y.
    c) Draw the reflection of the given shape in the line EF. Mark it Z.

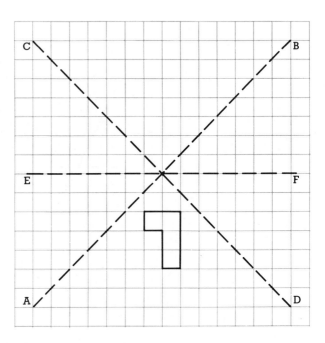

22. Draw the reflections of the given shape in each of the lines AB, CD and EF. Mark the reflections X, Y and Z respectively.

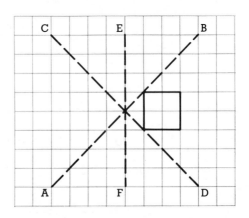

23. Draw the reflections of the given rectangle in each of the lines AB, CD, EF and GH. Mark the reflections W, X, Y and Z, respectively.

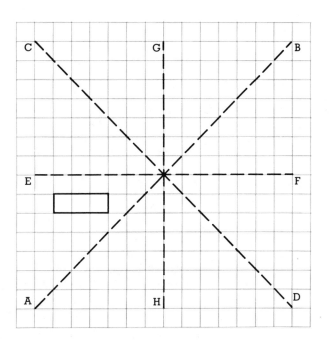

ROTATIONAL SYMMETRY

Some shapes have a form of symmetry that is not reflection, i.e. they do not have line symmetry but they can be rotated about a centre point and still look the same.

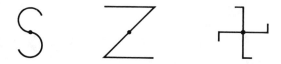

Shapes like these have rotational symmetry.

ORDER OF ROTATION SYMMETRY

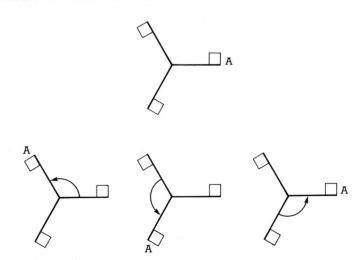

The shape in this diagram can be turned through a third of a revolution and still look the same. If we follow one point on the shape we can see that it requires three such turns to return it to its starting position.

This shape has rotational symmetry of order 3.

EXERCISE 4b   Give the order of rotational symmetry for each of these shapes.

1.

3.

5.

2.

4.

6.

ROTATIONS

We can change the position of a shape by reflecting it in a line. The reflected object is called the image.

We can also change the position of an object by rotating it about a point. The rotated object is again called the image.

In the following diagrams, the object triangle is rotated about a vertex A.

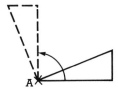

In this diagram, we get the image by rotating the object through 90° anticlockwise.

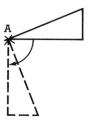

In this diagram, we get the image by rotating the object through 90° clockwise.

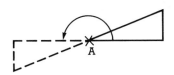

In this diagram, we get the image by rotating the object through 180° anticlockwise.

Notice that it is not enough to give just the size of the angle; the sense of turning (clockwise or anticlockwise) must also be stated.

The only case when the sense of turning is not required is for a rotation of 180°, because either a clockwise or an anticlockwise turn ends with the image in the same position.

FINDING THE IMAGE

In each of the previous rotations, the centre of rotation was a point on the object. If the centre of rotation is *not* part of the object, join one point of the object to the centre of rotation. Thinking of this new line as part of the object helps you to see where the image is after the required rotation.

To find the image of rectangle ABCD under a rotation of 90° clockwise about P, we can join A to P. Thinking of AP as part of the object, it is then easy to see where the image is.

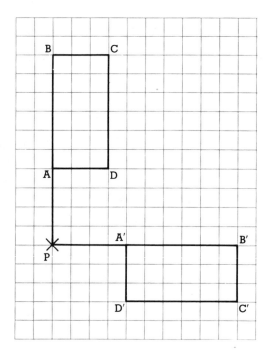

Another way to find the image uses tracing paper and a pin. Lay the tracing paper over the object. Trace the object and, with the pin in the centre of rotation, the tracing paper can be rotated through the required angle to give the position of the image.

EXERCISE 4c In each of the following questions copy the diagram on to squared paper. Draw the image of the given object under a rotation about P of the angle described.

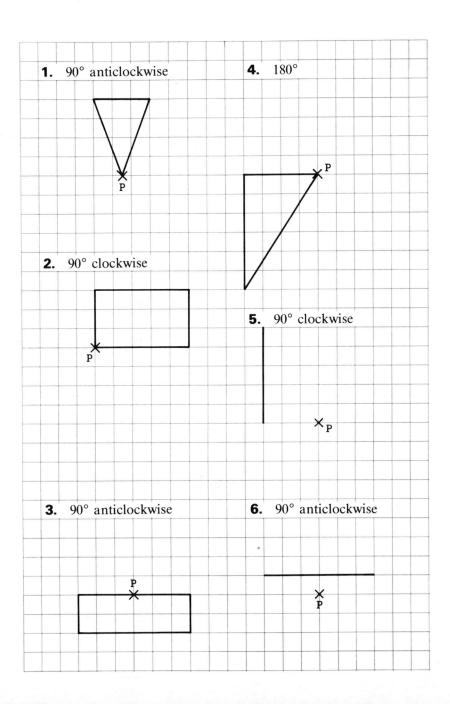

1. 90° anticlockwise

2. 90° clockwise

3. 90° anticlockwise

4. 180°

5. 90° clockwise

6. 90° anticlockwise

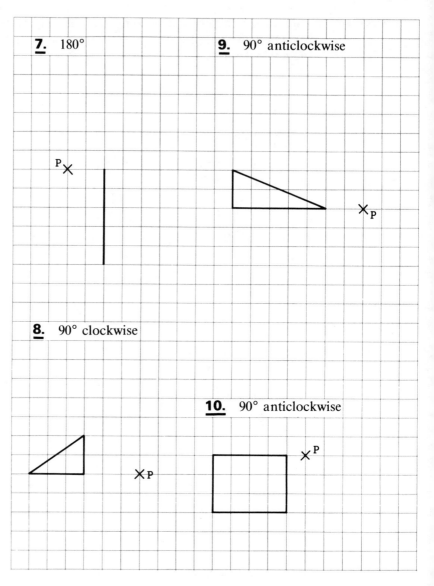

7. 180°

9. 90° anticlockwise

8. 90° clockwise

10. 90° anticlockwise

5 ALGEBRA

The first two exercises remind you of what you should already know.

SIMPLE EQUATIONS

EXERCISE 5a Solve the following equations. Remember that $4x$ means $4 \times x$.

1. $x + 3 = 7$ **4.** $x \div 3 = 2$ **7.** $a + 6 = 10$

2. $3x = 12$ **5.** $y - 4 = 9$ **8.** $4c = 12$

3. $5 - s = 3$ **6.** $5 + t = 7$ **9.** $d - 3 = 7$

You may have solved the equations above by guessing. Solve the next group of equations by following the rule: "Do the same thing to each side".

Solve $x + 3 = 8$

$$x + 3 = 8$$
Take 3 from each side $x = 5$

Solve the following equations. In each case write down what you are doing to each side.

10. $x + 4 = 6$ **13.** $5c = 15$ **16.** $z + 5 = 10$

11. $x - 7 = 9$ **14.** $y + 3 = 7$ **17.** $3y = 15$

12. $3x = 6$ **15.** $z - 4 = 5$ **18.** $x - 9 = 2$

Find the angle marked $x°$

The angles add up to 180° because they lie on a straight line.

$$x + 85 = 180$$

Take 85 from each side $x = 180 - 85$

$$= 95$$

The angle is 95°.

In each case, write down an equation and find the angle marked $x°$.

19.

21.

20.

22.

EQUATIONS NEEDING TWO STEPS

EXERCISE 5b Whatever you do to one side of the equation you must also do to the other.

Solve $2x + 1 = 7$

FIRST WE NEED TO GET THE x TERM ON ITS OWN.

$$2x + 1 = 7$$

Take 1 from each side $2x = 6$

Divide both sides by 2 $x = 3$

Solve the following equations, writing down what you are doing at each step. Make sure that you get the letter term on its own first.

1. $3x + 4 = 13$ **7.** $8p - 7 = 17$ **13.** $2s + 4 = 6$

2. $4x - 3 = 21$ **8.** $9x + 5 = 86$ **14.** $6a - 4 = 14$

3. $5c - 4 = 16$ **9.** $3x - 4 = 23$ **15.** $3y - 10 = 17$

4. $7x + 3 = 24$ **10.** $5q + 4 = 9$ **16.** $2 + 4x = 14$

5. $5x - 6 = 19$ **11.** $4x + 11 = 21$ **17.** $5s + 2 = 17$

6. $4y - 1 = 31$ **12.** $6x - 4 = 5$ **18.** $5s - 2 = 18$

EXPRESSIONS

We have seen that when an equation has an unknown letter in it, we can usually find the value of that letter.

An *expression* does not contain an "equals" sign. It is not possible to find the value of any letter in an expression.

All we can do is try to simplify an expression.

For instance, $2 \times x$ can be written as $2x$ and $x + x + x$ can be written as $3x$.

EXERCISE 5c   Which of the following are equations and which are expressions? Solve the ones that are equations.

1. $x + 6$ **4.** $x + y + 7$ **7.** $x^2 = 9$

2. $2a - 1 = 7$ **5.** $2y - 3 = 7$ **8.** $6 + z - 12$

3. $2a - 1$ **6.** $2y - 3$ **9.** $6 + z = 12$

Simplify the expressions

a) $4 \times p$ b) $2c + c$ c) $x \times x$

a) $4 \times p = 4p$

b) $2c + c = 3c$ (c is the same as $1c$)

c) $x \times x = x^2$

Simplify the following expressions.

10.	$z + z + z + z$	**14.**	$a + a + a$	**18.**	$x + 2x + 3x$
11.	$3y + 2y$	**15.**	$x \times x \times x \times x$	**19.**	$a \times a \times a$
12.	$5 \times t$	**16.**	$4y + y$	**20.**	$b + 2b + b$
13.	$s \times s$	**17.**	$9 \times b$	**21.**	$2 \times z$

LIKE AND UNLIKE TERMS

$x + 2x$ can be simplified to $3x$; x and $2x$ are like terms because they both contain simple x's.

$x + 2y$ cannot be simplified; x and $2y$ are unlike terms because one contains x and the other y.

$x + 3x - y$ can be partly simplified to $4x - y$.

EXERCISE 5d

Simplify, if possible,   a) $3x + 4x + 5$ b) $4x + 2y$

$3x$ AND $4x$ ARE LIKE TERMS,
5 AND $3x$ ARE UNLIKE.

a) $3x + 4x + 5 = 7x + 5$

$4x$ AND $2y$ ARE UNLIKE TERMS.

b) $4x + 2y$ cannot be simplified.

Simplify the following expressions where possible.

1.	$2x + 4 + 3x$	**6.**	$p + 2q$	**11.**	$a + b + c$
2.	$x + y$	**7.**	$z + 4 + z + 2$	**12.**	$4x - 3x + 7 - 5$
3.	$3x + 4 - 2x$	**8.**	$2x + y + 3x$	**13.**	$8x + 4 - 5x - 1$
4.	$3x - 2y$	**9.**	$4a + 3a - 2a - a$	**14.**	$4y + 6 - y - y$
5.	$9 - 2x + 1$	**10.**	$5c + 2d - 3c + d$	**15.**	$2x + 3y + 3x$

Simplify the equation $x + 2x + 3x = 12$ and solve it.

$$x + 2x + 3x = 12$$
$$6x = 12$$

Divide both sides by 6 $x = 2$

Simplify the following equations and solve them.

16. $x + x + x = 9$ **20.** $4b - b = 3$

17. $9y - 2y = 14$ **21.** $5c - 2c + 3c = 18$

18. $5a + 3a + 2a = 20$ **22.** $3x + 2x - x = 4$

19. $2x - x = 10$ **23.** $5z - 2z = 24$

Solve the equation $2z + 4z + 6 - 3 = 15$

(Collect the like terms first.)

$$2z + 4z + 6 - 3 = 15$$
$$6z + 3 = 15$$

Take 3 from each side $6z = 12$

Divide both sides by 6 $z = 2$

Solve the following equations.

24. $3a + a + 7 - 1 = 14$ **28.** $3y + 6y - 7y + 2 = 8$

25. $4x + 9 - 2x - 2 = 13$ **29.** $8s + 7s - 9 - 9s = 3$

26. $y + 6 + 2y = 15$ **30.** $a + 4 + 2a = 13$

27. $9 + x - 4 = 11$ **31.** $5 + x + 6 = 13$

32. Write down an equation and find the angle marked $x°$.

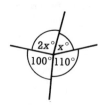

33. A cup of coffee cost x pence, a sandwich cost $3x$ pence and a bun cost x pence. The total cost was 160 pence. Write down an equation and find the value of x.

USING NEGATIVE NUMBERS

EXERCISE 5e

Simplify $-x + 3x$

$(-x$ means $-1x)$

Add 3

$$-x + 3x = 2x$$

Simplify

1. $-2x + 5x$ **6.** $-c + 2c$ **11.** $3y - 5y$

2. $-y - 2y$ **7.** $-5x - 2x$ **12.** $-3x + x$

3. $2a - 4a$ **8.** $2y - 7y$ **13.** $-z + z$

4. $-p + 2p$ **9.** $2x - 5x$ **14.** $-z - z$

5. $b - 3b$ **10.** $-a + 4a$ **15.** $z - z$

MORE SIMPLIFYING

> Simplify   a) $2 \times 4x$ b) $p \times q$ c) $4x \times 2x$
>
> a) $2 \times 4x = 8x$
>
> b) $p \times q = pq$
>
> c) $4x \times 2x = 8x^2$

Simplify

1.	$3 \times 2y$	**5.**	$7 \times 2z$	**9.**	$t \times 5t$
2.	$a \times b$	**6.**	$5t \times 3$	**10.**	$4 \times 6h$
3.	$y \times 5$	**7.**	$c \times d$	**11.**	$z \times y$
4.	$3x \times 5x$	**8.**	$3s \times 4s$	**12.**	$3r \times 2r$

Simplify where possible

13.	$8 \times 2x$	**18.**	$p + 2q$	**23.**	$3x \times x$
14.	$8 + 2x$	**19.**	$p \times 2q$	**24.**	$3x \times y$
15.	$4 + y - 3 + 2y$	**20.**	$p \times 2p$	**25.**	$3x + y$
16.	$6s - 3s + s$	**21.**	$7x + 4x$	**26.**	$3x + 3x$
17.	$9 + x - 7 - x$	**22.**	$7x + 4y$	**27.**	$3x + 3$

MULTIPLYING OUT BRACKETS

If an expression with brackets contains only numbers we work out its value by finding first the value of what is inside the brackets.

For example $2(4 + 5) = 2 \times 9$

$$= 18$$

If there is a letter in the bracket however, we cannot work out the value of what is inside the bracket. In some of these cases, it helps if we write the expression in a different way, e.g. $2(x + 6)$ means "two times whatever is in the brackets" so it means "two times x and two times 6".

$$2(x + 6) = 2 \times x + 2 \times 6$$
$$= 2x + 12$$

EXERCISE 5g

Write without brackets   a) $3(a + 4)$ b) $4(y - 3)$

a) $3(a + 4) = 3 \times a + 3 \times 4$

$= 3a + 12$

b) $4(y - 3) = 4 \times y - 4 \times 3$ $4 \times (-3) = -4 \times 3$

$= 4y - 12$

Write without brackets

1. $2(x + 5)$ **5.** $4(2 + y)$ **9.** $9(x + 2)$

2. $5(a - 4)$ **6.** $4(2 - y)$ **10.** $6(x - 3)$

3. $7(y + 1)$ **7.** $3(2x + 4)$ **11.** $5(5 + 2x)$

4. $3(z + 2)$ **8.** $4(3x - 5)$ **12.** $9(y - 6)$

EQUATIONS WITH BRACKETS

EXERCISE 5h

Write the equation without brackets, then solve it.

$$2(x + 4) = 12$$

$$2(x + 4) = 12$$

$$2x + 8 = 12$$

Take 8 from each side $2x = 4$

Divide both sides by 2 $x = 2$

Write each of the following equations without brackets and then solve it.

1. $2(x + 3) = 10$ **5.** $4(x + 1) = 20$

2. $3(x - 4) = 15$ **6.** $7(c - 3) = 28$

3. $6(2 + y) = 18$ **7.** $2(4 + x) = 12$

4. $2(4x + 3) = 14$ **8.** $3(a - 3) = 9$

9. $4(y + 4) = 20$ **12.** $2(x - 7) = 2$

10. $5(2 + x) = 25$ **13.** $3(3x + 1) = 21$

11. $2(2x + 1) = 10$ **14.** $6(x - 6) = 6$

SOLVING EQUATIONS BY TRIAL AND IMPROVEMENT

Some equations still need to be solved by guessing and testing.

EXERCISE 5i

Solve $x^2 + x = 11$

(x^2 and x are unlike terms so the equation cannot be simplified.)

Try $x = 2$ $x^2 + x = 2^2 + 2$

$= 4 + 2$

$= 6$ (too small)

Try $x = 3$ $x^2 + x = 9 + 3$

$= 12$ (too big, but only just)

Try $x = 2.8$ $x^2 + x = 2.8 \times 2.8 + 2.8$

$= 7.84 + 2.8$

$= 10.64$ (too small)

Try $x = 2.9$ $x^2 + x = 2.9 \times 2.9 + 2.9$

$= 8.41 + 2.9$

$= 11.31$ (too big)

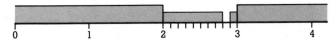

x lies between 2.8 and 2.9.

WE CAN GO ON AND TRY 2.85 IF WE
WANT A MORE ACCURATE ANSWER.

In each case, find to 1 d.p. two numbers between which the solution of the equation lies.

1. $x^2 = 7$

2. $x^2 = 28$

3. $x^2 + x = 14$

4. $x^2 - x = 25$

5. $z^2 = 40$

6. $y^2 + y = 4$

7. $x^2 - 2x = 7$

8. $s^2 = 8 + s$

9. $x^2 = 18$

10. $c^2 + c = 21$

11. $a^2 - a = 32$

12. $x^2 + 3x = 36$

6 ENLARGEMENTS

DRAWING ENLARGEMENTS

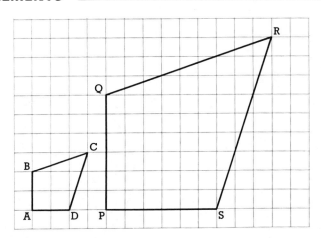

The quadrilateral on the right is an enlargement of the quadrilateral on the left. The enlargement is the same shape but each side of PQRS is three times as long as the corresponding side of ABCD.

The angles are the same, for example $\widehat{A} = 90°$ and $\widehat{P} = 90°$.

The size of the enlargement is given by the *scale factor*. The scale factor is a number. It tells us how many times as long as the original each line of the enlargement is. The scale factor in the above example is 3.

If we are asked to use a *scale factor of 2* we must draw each line *twice as long* as the original.

EXERCISE 6a For questions 1 to 4 copy each diagram on to squared paper and draw an enlargement of the shape with a scale factor of 2. Allow plenty of space for each enlargement.

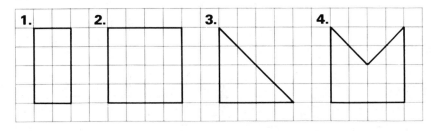

For questions 5 to 8 copy each diagram on to squared paper and draw an enlargement using a scale factor of 3.

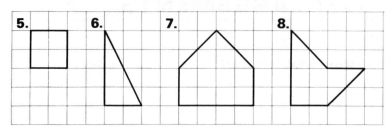

9.

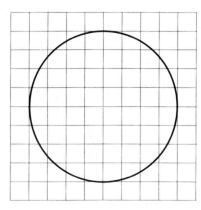

a) Measure the diameter of this circle.
b) What is the radius of this circle?
c) Draw an enlargement of this circle with a scale factor of 2.
d) What is the diameter of the enlarged circle?

Each of the figures A, B and C is part of a circle of radius 2 cm. For questions 10 to 15 draw the required figure on 1 cm squared paper and draw an enlargement using the given scale factor.

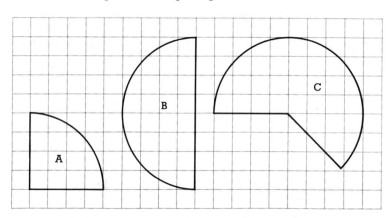

10. Draw figure A using a scale factor of 3.

11. Draw figure B using a scale factor of 2.

12. Draw figure C using a scale factor of 4.

13. Draw figure B using a scale factor of 5.

14. Draw figure A using a scale factor of 6.

15. Draw figure C using a scale factor of 2.

FINDING THE SCALE FACTOR

EXERCISE 6b

The large triangle is an enlargement of the small triangle. Find the scale factor.

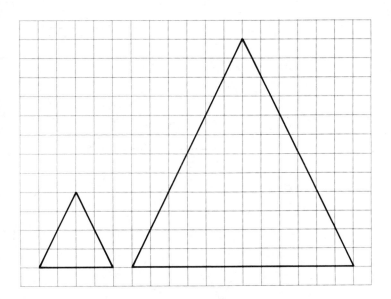

The length of the base of the small triangle is 2 cm.

The length of the base of the large triangle is 6 cm.

The scale factor is 3.

In each question from 1 to 4 the large figure is an enlargement of the small figure. Find the scale factor in each case.

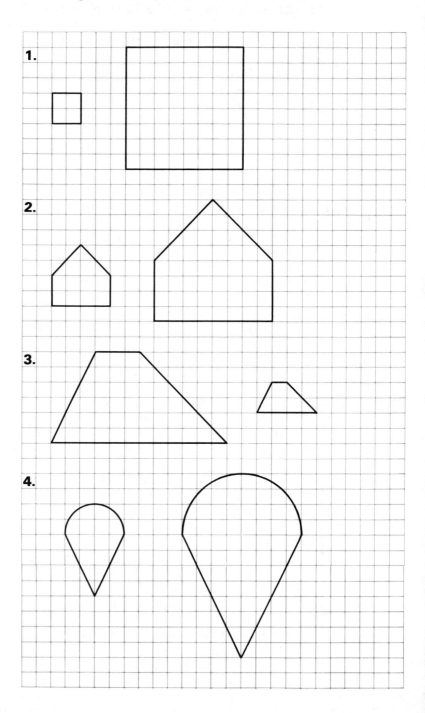

5. The sides of a square are each 3 cm long. An enlargement with a scale factor of 4 is to be drawn. How long should each side of the enlarged square be?

6. A rectangle measures 5 cm by 8 cm. An enlargement with a scale factor of 3 is to be drawn. What should the measurements of the enlarged rectangle be?

7. The lengths of the three sides of a triangle are 6 cm, 8 cm and 10 cm. An enlargement is to be drawn using a scale factor of 2.

a) What is the length of the longest side in the enlargement?
b) What is the length of the shortest side in the enlargement?

8. The sides of a square, when enlarged using a scale factor of 2, are each 14 cm long. How long were the sides of the original square?

For questions 9 to 11 the second diagram is an enlargement of the first.

9.

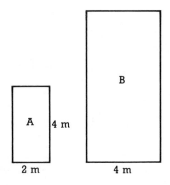

a) What is the scale factor?
b) How high is B?

10.

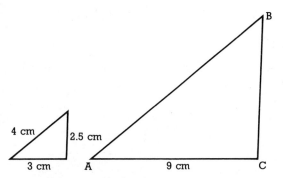

a) What is the scale factor?
b) Find the lengths of AB and BC.

11.

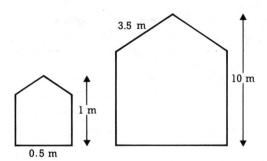

a) What is the scale factor?
b) How wide is the enlargement?
c) How long is a sloping line of the original?

7 ESSENTIAL GEOMETRY

This chapter revises some of the basic facts of geometry.

BASIC ANGLE FACTS

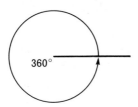

One complete revolution is 360°.

One quarter of a revolution is 90° and is called a right angle.

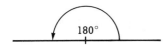

Half a revolution is 180°.

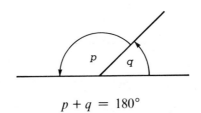

$$p + q = 180°$$

When two angles make half a revolution (i.e. make a straight line) they are called supplementary angles.

Angles on a straight line add up to 180°

75

When several angles together make a complete revolution they are called angles at a point.

$$p + q + r + s = 360°$$

Angles at a point add up to 360°.

When two straight lines cross, four angles are formed. The two angles that are opposite to each other are called vertically opposite angles.

Vertically opposite angles are equal.

EXERCISE 7a Calculate the size of the angle marked *x*.

1.

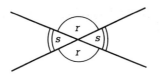

2.

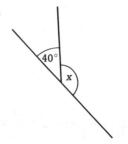

3.

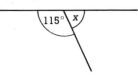

4.

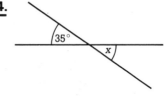

5.

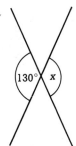

9.

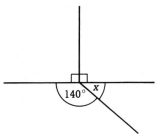

6.

10.

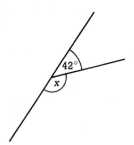

7.

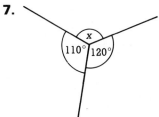

11.

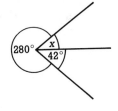

8.

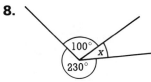

12.

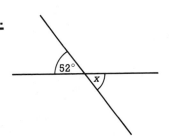

Find the size of the marked angle.

13.

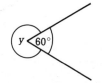

14.

15.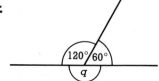

16.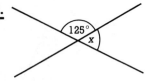

In the following questions you are given several alternative answers. Write down the letter that corresponds to the correct answer.

17.

The angle marked *x* is

A 130° B 50° C 230° D 70°

18.

The value of *x* is

A 60 B 120 C 45 D 90

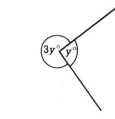

19.

The value of *y* is

A 180 B 120 C 90 D 60

20.

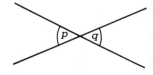

The angles marked *p* and *q*

A are supplementary B add up to 180° C are equal

21.

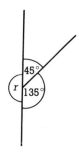

The angle marked *r* is

A 180°   **B** 135°   **C** 45°

ANGLES AND TRIANGLES

A triangle has three angles and three sides.
The corners are called vertices and are labelled with capital letters.
Each letter stands for the vertex and also for the angle,
i.e. in the diagram we can talk about the vertex A or the angle A.

We refer to the triangle as △ABC.

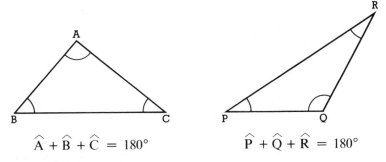

$$\widehat{A} + \widehat{B} + \widehat{C} = 180°$$ $$\widehat{P} + \widehat{Q} + \widehat{R} = 180°$$

Whatever the shape or size of the triangle,

the three angles of a triangle add up to 180°.

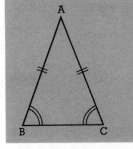

A triangle with two sides of equal length is called an *isosceles triangle*.
The angles at the base are the same size.

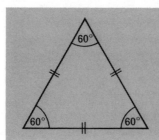

When a triangle has three equal sides it is called an *equilateral triangle* and each of its angles is 60°.

EXERCISE 7b Find the size of the angle marked *x*.

1.

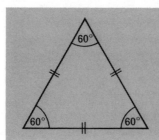

5.

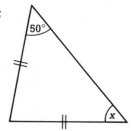

2.

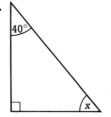

6.

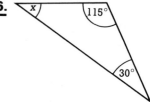

3.

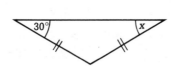

7.

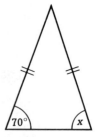

4.

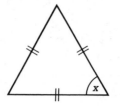

8.

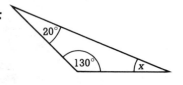

9.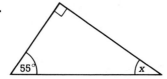

10.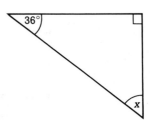

Find the size of the angle marked $x°$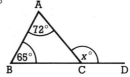

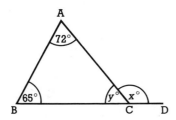

(First we need to find the unmarked angle at C. We will mark this $y°$.)

In △ABC, $65 + 72 + y = 180$

$137 + y = 180$

$y = 43$

BCD is a straight line, so $43 + x = 180$

$x = 137$

The size of the marked angle is 137°.

Find the size of the marked angle.

11.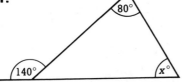

12.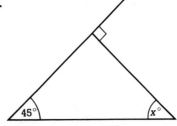

13.

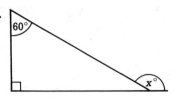

16.

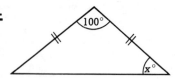

14.

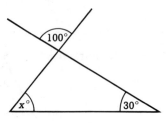

17.

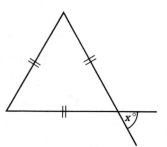

15.

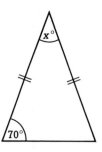

18.

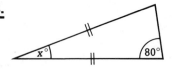

19.

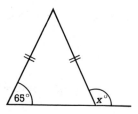

20.

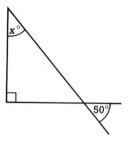

21.

22.

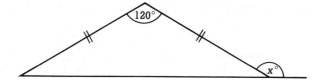

PARALLEL LINES AND ANGLES

Parallel lines are always the same distance apart.

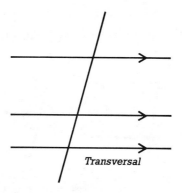

A line that cuts a set of parallel lines is called a *transversal* and it forms several angles.

These diagrams show pairs of corresponding angles.

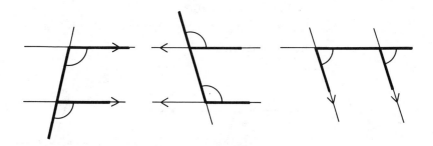

Corresponding angles are equal.

Corresponding angles can be recognised by looking for an F shape.

These diagrams show pairs of alternate angles.

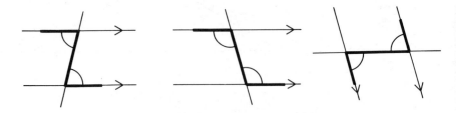

Alternate angles are equal.

Alternate angles can be recognised by looking for a Z shape.

These diagrams show pairs of interior angles.

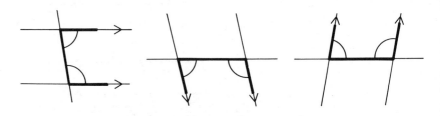

Interior angles add up to 180°.

Interior angles can be recognised by looking for a U shape.

EXERCISE 7c In each of the following diagrams one of the angles is shaded. Write down the angle which is

a) corresponding   b) alternate   c) interior,

to the shaded angle.

1.

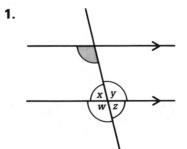

2.

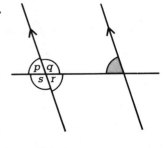

3.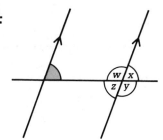

4.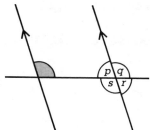

Find the size of the angle marked *x*.

5.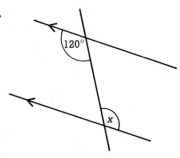

8.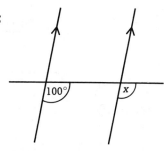

6.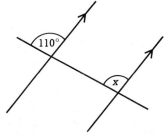

9.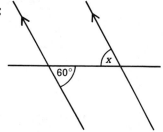

7.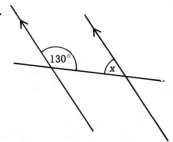

10.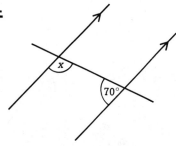

MIXED EXERCISES ━━━━━━━━━━━━━━━━━━━━━━━━━

EXERCISE 7d CALCULATIONS ━━━━━━━━━━━━━━━━━━━

Find the size of the marked angles. Use *any* facts that you know.

1.
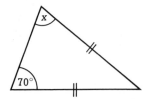

6.
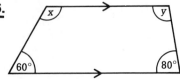

2.
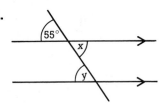

7.
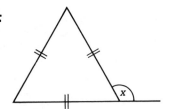

3.
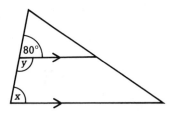

8.
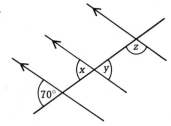

4.
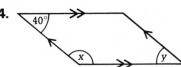

9.

5.
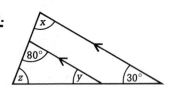

10.
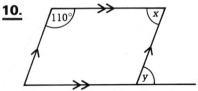

EXERCISE 7e In this exercise you have to find x. Several alternative answers are given. Write down the letter that corresponds to the correct answer.

1.

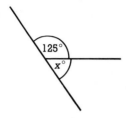

A 125   **B** 55   **C** 235

2.

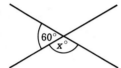

A 120   **B** 60   **C** 180

3.

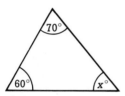

A 60   **B** 50   **C** 30

4.

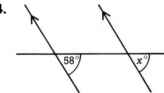

A 122   **B** 29   **C** 58

5.

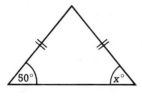

A 50   **B** 130   **C** 80

6.

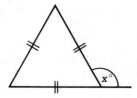

A 60   **B** 30   **C** 120

7. 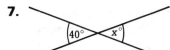   **A** 40   **B** 140   **C** 320

8. 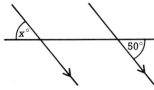   **A** 50   **B** 130   **C** 80

9.    **A** 90   **B** 110   **C** 20

EXERCISE 7f DRAWING

Use squared paper, ruler, compasses and a protractor. Note that the diagrams in this exercise are not drawn to scale.

1. Draw an equilateral triangle whose sides are 8 cm long. Measure the distance from one vertex to the opposite side. (Remember that this means the perpendicular distance.)

2.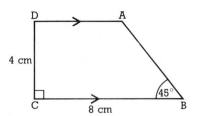

a) Make a full size copy of this figure.
b) *Calculate* the size of angle A.
c) *Measure* angle A.

3.

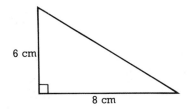

a) Make a full size copy of this figure.
b) Measure the longest side of the triangle.

4.

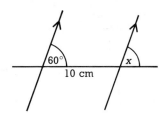

a) What is the size of the marked angle?
b) Copy this figure, making it full size.

5.

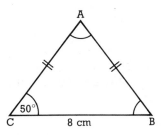

a) Write down the size of angle B.
b) Make a full size copy of this triangle.
c) *Calculate* the size of angle A.
d) *Measure* angle A.

6.

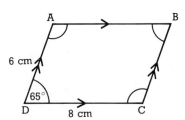

a) Write down the size of angle A.
b) Write down the size of angle C.
c) Make a full size copy of this parallelogram.
d) Measure angle B.

7.

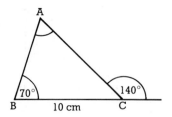

a) Calculate the unmarked angle at C.
b) Make a full size copy of this figure.
c) *Measure* angle A.
d) *Calculate* angle A.

8.

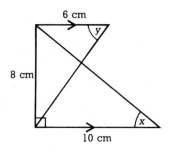

a) Make a full size copy of this figure.
b) Measure the size of the angle marked *x*.
c) Measure the size of the angle marked *y*.

8 PERCENTAGES

THE MEANING OF PERCENTAGE

Per cent means per hundred. For example 21 per cent, or 21%, means "21 per hundred". Now 21 per hundred can be written as $\frac{21}{100}$ which is 0.21,

i.e. a percentage can be expressed as a fraction or as a decimal.

EXPRESSING A PERCENTAGE AS A DECIMAL

EXERCISE 8a

Write 7% as a decimal

$$7\% = \frac{7}{100} = 0.07$$

Write each percentage as a decimal.

1.	3%	**6.**	16%	**11.**	90%	**16.**	20%
2.	15%	**7.**	44%	**12.**	65%	**17.**	81%
3.	40%	**8.**	50%	**13.**	7%	**18.**	100%
4.	25%	**9.**	24%	**14.**	37%	**19.**	30%
5.	75%	**10.**	5%	**15.**	45%	**20.**	28%

We know that $100\% = \frac{100}{100} = 1$ so a percentage bigger than 100% gives a decimal that is greater than 1.

Write 112% as a decimal.

$$112\% = \frac{112}{100} = 1.12$$

91

Write each percentage as a decimal.

21. 150%	**24.** 320%	**27.** 281%	**30.** 120%
22. 184%	**25.** 342%	**28.** 600%	**31.** 200%
23. 196%	**26.** 407%	**29.** 102%	**32.** 250%

EXPRESSING A DECIMAL AS A PERCENTAGE

A decimal can be expressed as a percentage. Remember that if there is a number in front of the decimal point we have more than 100%.

EXERCISE 8b

Express as a percentage a) 0.83   b) 2.51

a) $0.83 = \frac{83}{100} = 83\%$

SO, TO EXPRESS A DECIMAL AS A PERCENTAGE WE MULTIPLY THE DECIMAL BY 100.

b) $2.51 = 251\%$

Express as a percentage

1. 0.62	**4.** 2.05	**7.** 5.40	**10.** 0.30	**13.** 0.25
2. 0.11	**5.** 0.03	**8.** 0.10	**11.** 0.8	**14.** 0.75
3. 1.87	**6.** 1.30	**9.** 0.70	**12.** 0.32	**15.** 1.50

EXPRESSING A FRACTION AS A PERCENTAGE

Sometimes we need to express a fraction as a percentage and this can be done by first converting the fraction to a decimal.

A mixed number (e.g. $2\frac{4}{5}$) gives a percentage bigger than 100%.

It is useful to remember that

$$\frac{1}{2} = 50\% \qquad \frac{1}{4} = 25\% \qquad \frac{3}{4} = 75\%$$

EXERCISE 8c

> Express as a percentage a) $\frac{7}{20}$ b) $3\frac{4}{25}$
>
> a) $\frac{7}{20} = 0.35$
>
> $0.35 = 35\%$ (Multiply the decimal by 100)
>
> b) $3\frac{4}{25} = 3.16$ ($\boxed{4}\ \boxed{\div}\ \boxed{2}\ \boxed{5}\ \boxed{=}$ gives 0.16)
>
> $= 316\%$

Express each fraction as a percentage

1. $\frac{3}{10}$ **3.** $\frac{17}{50}$ **5.** $1\frac{13}{20}$ **7.** $\frac{11}{25}$

2. $2\frac{1}{2}$ **4.** $\frac{9}{10}$ **6.** $4\frac{3}{4}$ **8.** $1\frac{3}{100}$

PERCENTAGES, FRACTIONS AND DECIMALS

EXERCISE 8d **1.** Express $\frac{6}{25}$ as a) a decimal   b) a percentage

2. Express 60% as a) a fraction   b) a decimal

3. Express 0.81 as a) a fraction   b) a percentage

Copy and complete the following table. The working needed is similar to the working required for questions 1 to 3.

	Fraction	Percentage	Decimal
4.		50%	
5.	$\frac{3}{4}$		
6.			0.25
7.		20%	
8.			0.8

PROBLEMS INVOLVING 100%

When we have 100% of a quantity we have the whole of the quantity. If 40% of the pupils in a class are boys then $(100-40)\%$ of the pupils are girls, i.e. 60% are girls.

EXERCISE 8e

If Alan spends 82% of his weekly money, what percentage does he save?

Alan saves $(100-82)\%$

$= 18\%$ of his money.

1. On Monday, 97% of the pupils are in school. What percentage of the pupils are absent?

2. When Mr Adams ordered a sofa, he paid a deposit of 15% of its price. What percentage of its price is there still to pay?

3. Philip is asleep for 28% of any 24 hour day. For what percentage of the day is he awake?

4. In a train to London, 93% of the seats are filled. What percentage of the seats are empty?

5. A family spends 54% of its income on food and 20% on clothes. What percentage is not spent on food or clothes?

6. In an election, Mr Garfield and Mrs Lincoln each received 48% of the votes and the remaining voting papers were spoiled. What percentage of the voting papers were spoiled?

7. Of a set of books, 6% are damaged in some way and cannot be used. What percentage of the books are usable?

8. Light bulbs made in a factory are tested and, in one batch, 8% are found to be faulty. What percentage are not faulty?

9. At a jumble sale, 64% of the jumble is sold during the sale, 24% is taken away afterwards by a dealer and the rest is rubbish. What percentage of the jumble is rubbish?

PERCENTAGES OF QUANTITIES

Percentages are not of much use on their own. A percentage *of something* is what really matters. A 5% rise in wages, for example, means nothing until we know what it is 5% of, e.g. 5% of £80.

EXERCISE 8f

Find 15% of 20 days

$$15\% = 0.15$$
$$15\% \text{ of 20 days} = 0.15 \times 20 \text{ days} \quad (\text{"of" means } \times)$$
$$= 3 \text{ days}$$

Use a calculator if necessary to find

1. 5% of 40 p

6. 20% of £5

11. 75% of 80 cm

2. 10% of 600 m

7. 25% of 4 p

12. 63% of 900 km

3. 15% of 60 m

8. 12% of £100

13. 35% of £80

4. 32% of £25

9. 27% of 250 g

14. 2% of 300 mm

5. 75% of 16 cm

10. 36% of 75 m

15. 95% of 240 p

16. 40% of £15

21. 6% of 250 m

26. 1% of 4000 m

17. 50% of 28 g

22. 20% of 12 km

27. 32% of 50 kg

18. 80% of £45

23. 25% of 8 p

28. 86% of 450 p

19. 85% of 8000 kg

24. 50% of 18 p

29. 5% of 320 m

20. 4% of 200 km

25. 8% of £50

30. 16% of 125 m

In questions 31 to 33, several alternative answers are given. Write down the letter that corresponds to the correct answer.

31. 10% of 50 m is

    A 500 m   **B** 5 m   **C** 10 m   **D** 25 m

32. 200% of 80 kg is

    A 40 kg   **B** 16 kg   **C** 160 kg   **D** 200 kg

33. 50% of 24 m is

    A 48 m   **B** 12 m   **C** 120 m   **D** 2.4 m

PROBLEMS

EXERCISE 8g

> Mr Sharp pays a deposit of 15% on a second-hand car whose cost is £900. How much is the deposit?
>
> The deposit is 15% of £900
>
> $$15\% = 0.15$$
>
> $$\therefore \quad 15\% \text{ of } £900 = £(0.15 \times 900)$$
>
> $$= £135$$

1. In a greengrocer's shop, a box contains 80 oranges.
If 5% of the oranges are bad, how many bad oranges are there?

2. In a biology examination there were 70 candidates and 90% passed.
How many pupils passed the examination?

3. During an epidemic, 24% of the pupils of a primary school caught chickenpox. If there were 300 pupils in the school, how many caught chickenpox?

4. In a local election, 32% of the electorate did not vote.
There were 2500 on the electoral list. How many did not vote?

5. Seven years ago Mrs Allen bought a car that cost £1100. If she is now selling it for 35% of the cost price, what is her selling price?

6. Of the pupils in a school 49% are boys. There are 1200 pupils in the school altogether. How many boys are there?

7. Carol saves 30% of the money her grandmother gives her. For her birthday this year her grandmother has given her £2. How much does Carol save this time?

8. 72% of the vehicles passing the school gate are cars. If 250 vehicles pass the gate in one day, how many of them are cars?

9. Of the residents in a block of flats, 12% are under fifteen years of age. If 125 people live in the block, how many of them are under fifteen?

10. 62% of the population of a town are over 40 years old. The population is 12 600. How many people over 40 years old live in the town?

EXPRESSING ONE QUANTITY AS A PERCENTAGE OF ANOTHER

We start by expressing the first quantity as a fraction of the other and then change the fraction into a percentage.

EXERCISE 8h

Express 3 m as a percentage of 12 m

$$3 \text{ m} = \frac{3}{12} \text{ of } 12 \text{ m}$$

$$\frac{3}{12} = 0.25$$

$$= 25\%$$

3 m = 25% of 12 m

1. Express 2 p as a percentage of 10 p.

2. Express 8 m as a percentage of 25 m.

3. Express 5 g as a percentage of 20 g.

4. Express £15 as a percentage of £50.

5. Express 3 g as a percentage of 75 g.

6. Express 18 m as a percentage of 60 m.

7. Express 25 kg as a percentage of 125 kg.

8. Express 45 cm as a percentage of 50 cm.

Express the first quantity as a percentage of the second one.

9.	32 p; 50 p	**13.**	45 m; 180 m	**17.**	9 hours; 24 hours
10.	12 kg; 25 kg	**14.**	£6; £60	**18.**	36 g; 120 g
11.	13 m; 10 m	**15.**	11 cm; 55 cm	**19.**	65 miles; 130 miles
12.	14 p; 56 p	**16.**	4 km; 50 km	**20.**	17 p; 20 p

MIXED UNITS

Sometimes the two quantities are expressed in different units, so one of the units has to be changed. It is usually easier to work with the smaller unit. For example, if we are given centimetres and metres then we work in centimetres.

EXERCISE 8i

Express 63 p as a percentage of £3

$$£3 = 300 \text{ p}$$
$$63 \text{ p} = \frac{63}{300} \text{ of } £3$$
$$\frac{63}{300} = 0.21$$
$$= 21\%$$

63 p is 21% of £3

1. Express 16 cm as a percentage of 4 m.

2. Express 40 p as a percentage of £2.

3. Express 4 cm as a percentage of 1 m.

4. Express 240 g as a percentage of 2 kg.

5. Express 60 m as a percentage of 3 km.

6. Express 72 p as a percentage of £3.60.

7. Express 14 days as a percentage of 10 weeks.

8. Express 380 m as a percentage of 2 km.

We do not always get a decimal with an exact value.

Express £25 as a percentage of £75, giving your answer correct to 1 decimal place.

$$\frac{25}{75} = 0.3333$$
$$= 33.3\vdots 3\%$$
£25 = 33.3% of £75   (correct to 1 d.p.)

Express the first quantity as a percentage of the second one. Where necessary give your answer correct to 1 d.p.

9. 3 cm; 7 cm	**13.** 4 m; 680 cm	**17.** 4 kg; 3 kg
10. 14 g; 21 g	**14.** 5 g; 6 g	**18.** 8 g; 36 g
11. 40 m; 2 km	**15.** 5 cm; 80 mm	**19.** 2 m; 11 m
12. £3; £11	**16.** 7 p; 9 p	**20.** 120 cm; 7 m

PROBLEMS

EXERCISE 8j

In a class of 25 pupils there are 14 girls. What percentage of the pupils are girls?

$\frac{14}{25}$ of the pupils are girls

$$\frac{14}{25} = 0.56$$

$$= 56\%$$

56% of the pupils are girls.

1. In a mathematics lesson, 12 pupils are writing in pencil. There are 25 pupils in the class. What percentage of them are writing in pencil?

2. In a cricket match, John made 17 runs and the total number of runs scored was 85. Express the number of runs scored by John as a percentage of the total.

3. The profit from selling a picture is £800. Mr Adams gets £300 of it and his wife gets £500. What percentage of the profit does Mr Adams receive and what percentage does his wife receive?

4. A man goes on a 50 mile journey. If he travels for 16 miles on a motorway, what percentage of the journey is this?

5. In a box containing 120 eggs, 6 are bad. What percentage of the eggs are good?

6. Mark's journey to school is 1500 m. He runs 120 m and walks the rest. What percentage of the whole distance does he run?

7. Andrew sleeps for eight hours of a twenty-four hour day. For what percentage of the day is he awake?

8. At the beginning of the day, a greengrocer's shop has 200 oranges. If 48 are sold during the day what percentage of the oranges are sold?

DISCOUNT

We are familiar with large notices in shops at sale time which declare "10% off all marked prices" or "50% off all dresses on this rail". These are examples of what we call *discount*.

Discount is often given to encourage prompt payment, e.g. a builder's merchant may offer a discount of 5% if bills are paid within 7 days, $2\frac{1}{2}$% if paid within 14 days, otherwise strictly net, i.e. the full amount must be paid.

For example, 5% discount on a bill of £100 is £(0.05×100) = £5 and $2\frac{1}{2}$% discount is half as much, i.e. £2.50. So payment within 7 days reduces the bill to £95 and payment within 14 days reduces it to £97.50.

After 14 days the full £100 is charged.

EXERCISE 8k

Brian bought a motor-bike with a marked price of £250. Because he paid cash he was given a discount of 8%. How much was the discount and how much did Brian pay for the bike?

The discount was 8% of the marked price

i.e. $\qquad$ 8% × £250

$\qquad$ = £0.08 × 250

$\qquad$ = £20

The cost of the bike was £250 − £20 = £230.

Find the value of the discount offered on each of the articles in questions 1 to 7.

	Article	Marked Price	Discount
1.	Record	£6	30%
2.	Jacket	£39.50	50%

Article	Marked Price	Discount
3. Jumper	£24	60%
4. Television	£280	15%
5. Carpet	£120	35%
6. Christmas cards	80 p	20%
7. Bedroom suite	£1500	25%

In each question from 8 to 11 find the price of the article when it is sold at the given discount.

Article	Marked Price	Discount
8. Bicycle	£110	10%
9. Video	£660	20%
10. Refrigerator	£150	15%
11. Hi-fi unit	£475	50%

12. In a sale a dress marked £24 is offered at a discount of 25%. Find the sale price.

13. A builder's merchant offers a discount of 5% for payment within 7 days. How much is saved by paying a bill for £720 within 7 days?

14. A sale discount of 30% is given on a dining suite marked £640. How much is the discount and how much does the suite cost in the sale?

OTHER PERCENTAGE CHANGES

The values of most everyday quantities change as time passes. For example, the cost of goods changes (nearly always increasing!), the number of people living in a particular area changes, vehicle insurance premiums change, and so on.

These changes are often expressed as percentages. We are all familiar with news items such as

"Bus fares increase by 5%"
"Workforce reduced by 8%"
"School roll down by 10%"
"Wage increase of $7\frac{1}{2}$% agreed"

> When a quantity increases or decreases, the change is expressed as a percentage of the *original* value of that quantity, i.e. the value *before* the change took place.

For example, to find the percentage increase when a bus fare goes up by 2 p, from 20 p to 22 p, we find 2 p as a percentage of 20 p.

Similarly if a pony that cost £850 is sold two years later at a profit of 30%, the profit is 30% of £850.

If we are to understand statements about percentage changes we need to know the various words that are used.
An increase can be described as
gain, profit, surcharge, appreciation, inflation.
For a decrease some of the words used are
loss, discount, reduction, depreciation.

EXERCISE 8I

Train fares are to be increased by 6%. How much extra will have to be paid on a fare of £8.50? How much will the new fare be?

The percentage increase is 6% of £8.50

$$= £(0.06 \times 8.50)$$

$$= £0.51$$

$$= 51 \text{ p}$$

The new fare is   £8.50 + 51 p = £9.01.

1. Nick earns £16 from his Saturday job. If he is given a rise of 5% how much extra will he earn?

2. The Smith family bought a car for £8000 and sold it two years later at a loss of 32%. How much did they lose?

3. Jane Frank's house cost £40 000 when she bought it. Since then the house has appreciated by 30%. Find the increase in value. What is her house worth now?

4. A shopkeeper buys an article for £140 and sells it at a profit of 35%. How much does she gain? How much does she sell the article for?

5. Ann sold a coat to Shareen at a loss of 20%. If Ann paid £40 for the coat how much did Shareen pay Ann?

6. A farmer bought a calf for £150 and sold it when fully grown at a profit of 300%. For how much did he sell the animal?

7. The length of a pair of new curtains was 2 m. When they were washed they shrank by 5% of their length. Find the length of the curtains after they had been washed.

8. The prices quoted in a holiday brochure are subject to a surcharge of 12% if a single room is requested. If a holiday is priced at £170, how much does single accommodation cost?

9. A mother's help is paid £3 an hour. If her wage is increased by 6% what is her new hourly rate?

10. An airline gives a reduction of 20% on fares for children aged 2 to 12. Find the child fare when the adult fare is £120.

A car is bought for £4000 and sold a year later for £3400. What is the percentage loss?

Loss = £4000 − £3400 = £600

Original price = £4000

$$£600 = \frac{600}{4000} \text{ of } £4000$$

$$\frac{600}{4000} = 0.15$$

$$= 15\%$$

The percentage loss is 15%.

11. A dealer buys a picture for £2000 and sells it for £3000. What is his percentage profit?

12. A bicycle that was bought for £140 is later sold for £80. What is the percentage loss?

13. Find the percentage profit if an article costing 75 p is sold for £1.

14. The Brown family booked a package holiday costing £860. Before they left a surcharge of £43 was added to their bill. What was the percentage surcharge?

15. A sale ticket reads:

> Original price £5
> Sale price £4

Find the percentage reduction.

16. A jeweller buys a gold ring for £250 and sells it for £400. What is his percentage gain?

17. Mike bought a new motor bike for £1200. A year later it was worth only £1000. Find the percentage depreciation.

18. In a supermarket the price of a jar of coffee goes up from £1.70 to £1.87. What is the percentage increase in price?

19. Anwar saw this notice in the window of "Sight and Sound"

> This week only
>   YANSO HIFI UNIT £162
> Usual price £200

What is the percentage reduction this week?

VALUE ADDED TAX

Value added tax or VAT is a government tax which is added to most of the things we buy and also to many services. The rate of tax is decided from time to time by the Chancellor of the Exchequer.

EXERCISE 8m

Find the purchase price of a camera marked £160 + VAT assuming that the rate of value added tax is 15%.

VAT is 15% of the marked price

i.e. 0.15 of the marked price

$$\text{VAT} = £(0.15 \times 160)$$

$$= £24$$

$\therefore$ Purchase price = marked price + VAT

$$= £160 + £24$$

$$= £184$$

In questions 1 to 8 find the purchase price of the given article or service assuming that the rate of value added tax is 15%.

1. A pair of shoes costing £26 + VAT.

2. A light fitting costing £62 + VAT.

3. A football marked £12.40 + VAT.

4. A calculator marked £12.80 + VAT.

5. Servicing a car for £56.60 + VAT.

6. A telephone bill amounting to £48.40 + VAT.

7. A dining room suite marked £1600 + VAT.

8. A car costing £6400 + VAT.

MIXED EXERCISES

EXERCISE 8n **1.** Express 8% as   a) a fraction   b) a decimal.

2. Express $\frac{3}{5}$ as   a) a decimal   b) a percentage.

3. Find 45% of 40 p.

4. Express 1.32 as a percentage.

5. 65% of the vehicles passing along a major road are lorries.
If 300 vehicles pass, how many of them are lorries?

6. If 8% of a box of ballpoint pens will not write, what percentage
of the pens are usable?

7. In a box of 200 bananas, 14 bananas are bad. What percentage
of the bananas are bad?

8. A second hand car dealer buys a car for £4500 and sells it at a
loss of 8%. How much does he lose?

EXERCISE 8p **1.** Express 26% as a decimal.

2. Express $\frac{13}{20}$ as a percentage.

3. Find 75% of £4.40.

4. Express 37% as a decimal.

5. In school, 9% of the time is spent on mathematics lessons.
What percentage of the time is *not* spent on mathematics
lessons?

6. The Martin family spend 20% of their holiday time in travelling.
Their holiday lasts ten days. How long do they spend
travelling?

7. The Martin family take 80 kg of luggage with them on holiday.
Angela Martin takes 16 kg. What percentage is this of the total
amount of luggage?

8. The Martin family take £500 spending money on holiday.
They spend £400. What percentage of their spending money is
left?

9. Bicycles bought for £80 are sold for £108. Find the percentage gain.

10. Find the cash price of a record album marked £18.60 plus VAT at 15%.

EXERCISE 8q In each question, several alternative answers are given. Write down the letter that corresponds to the correct answer.

1. Expressed as a decimal, 30% is

    A 3.0   **B** 30.0   **C** 0.3   **D** 0.03

2. Expressed as a percentage, $\frac{1}{5}$ is

    A 2%   **B** 5%   **C** 20%   **D** 50%

3. 16% of 200 cm is

    A 16 cm   **B** 32 cm   **C** 8 cm   **D** 320 cm

4. In a school election, 30% vote for Mary and 40% vote for Anne. The percentage who vote for neither Mary nor Anne is

    A 70%   **B** 10%   **C** 40%   **D** 30%

5. Gavin had 70 p in his pocket. He spent 7 p. The percentage of his money that he spent was

    A 50%   **B** 7%   **C** 10%   **D** 70%

6. A radio bought for £40 and sold for £30 results in a loss of

    A 10%   **B** 30%   **C** 75%   **D** 25%

7. A shopkeeper buys an article for £44 and sells it to give a profit of 50%. The selling price is

    A £66   **B** £22   **C** £88   **D** £94

8. In one innings of a cricket match Jack Shore made 50% of the total number of runs. Which of the following statements must be true?

    A The team made 100 runs.   **C** Jack Shore made 50 runs.

    B Jack Shore made half the runs.   **D** Only two people batted.

9 PROBABILITY

MEASURING CHANCE

If you toss an ordinary coin, it will land either heads up or tails up. If the coin is unbiased, these two possibilities (or events) are equally likely.

The chance of the coin landing heads up is 1 out of 2 equally likely events. This can be written as the fraction $\frac{1}{2}$.

Probability is the word used to measure chance.

Therefore the probability that the coin will land heads up is $\frac{1}{2}$.

In general, the probability that any event happens is the fraction

$$\frac{\text{Number of ways in which the event can happen}}{\text{Total number of equally likely events}}$$

If an event is impossible, for example that a pen taken from a box of red pens is blue, then the probability that it happens is zero.

If an event is certain, for example that a pen taken from a box of red pens is red, then the probability that it happens is one.

Most events fall somewhere between impossible and certain. Probabilities are easier to compare if they are written as decimals and this scale shows the complete range of probabilities.

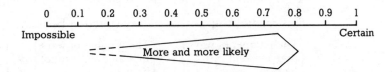

EXERCISE 9a Give each probability as a decimal, correct to 2 d.p. if necessary.

1. One letter is chosen at random from the word FOOD. ('Random' means that any possibility is equally likely.)
   a) How many equally likely choices are there?
   b) How many of these give the letter O?
   c) What is the probability that the letter O will be chosen?

2. This bag contains three black discs and two white discs. One disc is taken out of the bag at random.

a) How many equally likely choices are there for the disc that is removed?

b) How many of the choices in (a) give a white disc?

c) What is the probability of removing a white disc from the bag?

d) What is the probability that a red disc is taken out of this bag?

3. An ordinary six-sided dice is rolled. What is the probability that the score is

a) six   c) more than six e) greater than four

b) less than three d) six or less   f) zero?

4. An ordinary six-sided dice is thrown. Which is more likely to happen, a score that is less than three or a score that is greater than four? Use your answers to question 3.

PROBABILITY THAT AN EVENT DOES NOT HAPPEN

If one card is randomly removed from an ordinary pack of 52 playing cards, then the probability that it is a club is $\frac{13}{52}$, i.e. 0.25

Now there are 39 cards that are *not* clubs,

so the probability that the card is not a club is $\frac{39}{52} = 0.75$

But $0.25 + 0.75 = 1$.

i.e. Probability (a club) + Probability (not a club) = 1

This relationship is true in any situation because,

$$\left\{ \begin{matrix} \text{The number of ways} \\ \text{that an event can} \\ \text{happen} \end{matrix} \right\} + \left\{ \begin{matrix} \text{The number of ways} \\ \text{that an event cannot} \\ \text{happen} \end{matrix} \right\} = \left\{ \begin{matrix} \text{The total number} \\ \text{of possibilities} \end{matrix} \right\}$$

This means that

Probability (an event happens)

    + Probability (same event does not happen) = 1

or, to put it another way,

> Probability (an event doesn't happen)
> = 1 − Probability (same event happens)

EXERCISE 9b

A letter is chosen at random from the letters of the word **PROBABILITY**. What is the probability that the letter is not B?

There are 11 letters and 2 of them are B's,

so the probability that the letter is B is $\frac{2}{11} = 0.181\ldots$

Therefore the probability that the letter is not B is

$$1 - 0.181$$

$$= 0.819$$

$$= 0.82 \text{ correct to 2 d.p.}$$

This problem can also be solved without using the result above. Since 9 of the 11 letters are not B's the probability that the letter is not B is $\frac{9}{11}$, i.e. 0.82 correct to 2 d.p.

Give your answers in decimal form, correct to two decimal places where necessary.

1. A number is chosen at random from the first 20 whole numbers. What is the probability that it is not a prime number?

2. A card is drawn at random from an ordinary pack of playing cards. What is the probability that it is not a two?

3. One letter is chosen at random from the letters of the alphabet. What is the probability that it is not a vowel?

4. A box of 60 coloured crayons contains a mixture of colours, 10 of which are red. If one crayon is removed at random, what is the probability that it is not red?

5. A number is chosen at random from the first 10 whole numbers. What is the probability that it is not exactly divisible by 3?

6. One letter is chosen at random from the letters of the word ALPHABET. What is the probability that it is not a vowel?

7. In a raffle, 500 tickets are sold. If you buy 20 tickets, what is the probability that you will not win first prize?

8. If you throw an ordinary six-sided dice, what is the probability that you will not get a score of 5 or more?

9. There are 200 packets hidden in a lucky dip. Five packets contain £1 and the rest contain 1 p. What is the probability that you will not draw out a packet containing £1?

10. When an ordinary pack of playing cards is cut, what is the probability that the card showing is not a picture card? (The picture cards are the jacks, queens and kings.)

11. A letter is chosen at random from the letters of the word SUCCESSION. What is the probability that the letter is

a) N   b) S   c) a vowel   d) not S?

12. A card is drawn at random from an ordinary pack of playing cards. What is the probability that it is

a) an ace   c) not a club
b) a spade   d) not a seven or an eight?

13. A bag contains a set of snooker balls (i.e. 15 red and 1 each of the following colours: white, yellow, green, brown, blue, pink and black). What is the probability that one ball removed at random is

a) red   b) not red   c) black   d) not red or white?

14. There are 60 cars in the station car park. Of the cars, 22 are British made, 24 are Japanese made and the rest are European but not British. What is the probability that the first car to leave is   a) Japanese   c) European but not British
                              b) not British   d) American?

POSSIBILITY SPACE FOR TWO EVENTS

Suppose a 2 p coin and a 10 p coin are tossed together. One possibility is that the 2 p coin will land head up and that the 10 p coin will also land head up.

If we use H for a head on the 2 p coin and *H* for a head on the 10 p coin, we can write this possibility more briefly as the ordered pair (H, *H*).

To list all the possibilities, an organized approach is necessary, otherwise we may miss some. We use a table called a *possibility space*. The possibilities for the 10 p coin are written across the top and the possibilities for the 2 p coin are written down the side.

10 p coin

	H	*T*
H		
T		

2 p coin

When both coins are tossed we can see all the combinations of heads and tails that are possible and then fill in the table.

10 p coin

	H	*T*
H	(H, *H*)	(H, *T*)
T	(T, *H*)	(T, *T*)

2 p coin

EXERCISE 9c 1. Two bags each contain three white counters and two black counters. One counter is removed at random from each bag. Copy and complete the following possibility space for the possible combinations of two counters.

1st bag

		○	○	○	●	●
	○	(○,○)	(○,○)	(○,○)	(●,○)	
	○					
2nd bag	○					
	●					(●,●)
	●	(○,●)				

2. An ordinary six-sided dice is tossed and a 10 p coin is tossed. Copy and complete the following possibility space.

Dice

		1	2	3	4	5	6
	H		(H,2)				
10 p coin							
	T				(T,4)		

3. One bag contains two red counters, one yellow counter and one blue counter. Another bag contains two yellow counters, one red counter and one blue counter. One counter is taken at random from each bag. Copy and complete the following possibility space.

1st bag

	R	R	Y	B
R		(R, R)		
Y				(B, Y)
Y				
B	(R, B)			

2nd bag

4. A top like the one in the diagram is spun twice. Copy and complete the possibility space.

1st spin

	1	2	3
1			
2			
3			

2nd spin

5. A boy goes into a shop to buy a pencil and a rubber. He has a choice of a red, a green or a yellow pencil and a round, a square or a triangular shaped rubber. Make your own possibility space for the possible combinations of one pencil and one rubber that he could buy.

USING A POSSIBILITY SPACE

We can use a possibility space to find a probability because we can count all the possible events and also those that we are interested in.

EXERCISE 9d

Two ordinary six-sided dice are tossed. Draw up a possibility space showing all the possible combinations in which the dice may land.

Use the possibility space to find the probability that at least one six is thrown.

1st dice

		1	2	3	4	5	6
	1	1, 1	1, 2	1, 3	1, 4	1, 5	(1, 6)
	2	2, 1	2, 2	2, 3	2, 4	2, 5	(2, 6)
	3	3, 1	3, 2	3, 3	3, 4	3, 5	(3, 6)
2nd dice	4	4, 1	4, 2	4, 3	4, 4	4, 5	(4, 6)
	5	5, 1	5, 2	5, 3	5, 4	5, 5	(5, 6)
	6	(6, 1)	(6, 2)	(6, 3)	(6, 4)	(6, 5)	(6, 6)

There are 36 entries in the table and 11 of these give at least one six.

Probability of at least one six = $\frac{11}{36}$ = 0.31 to 2 d.p.

In questions 1 to 9 give probabilities as decimals correct to 2 d.p.

1. Use the possibility space in the example on the opposite page to find the probability of throwing

a) a total score of 5   c) a total score of less than 5.

b) a double   d) a total score greater than 4.

2. Use the possibility space for question 1 of Exercise 9c to find the probability that the two counters removed

a) are both black   b) contain at least one black.

3. Use the possibility space for question 2 of Exercise 9c to find the probability that the coin lands heads up and the dice gives a score that is less than 3.

4. Use the possibility space for question 3 of Exercise 9c to find the probability that the two counters removed are

a) both blue

b) both red

c) one blue and one red

d) such that at least one is red.

5. A 5 p coin and a 1 p coin are tossed together. Make your own possibility space for the combinations in which they can land. Find the probability of getting two heads.

6. A six-sided dice has two of its faces blank and the other faces are numbered 1, 3, 4 and 6. This dice is tossed with an ordinary six-sided dice (faces numbered 1, 2, 3, 4, 5, 6). Make a possibility space for the ways in which the two dice can land and use it to find the probability of getting a total score of

a) 6   b) 10   c) 1   d) at least 6.

7. One bag of coins contains three 10 p coins and two 50 p coins. Another bag contains one 10 p coin and one 50 p coin. One coin is removed at random from each bag. Make a possibility space and use it to find the probability that a 50 p coin is taken from each bag.

8. One bookshelf contains two storybooks and three textbooks. The next shelf holds three storybooks and one text book. Draw a possibility space showing the various ways in which you could pick up a pair of books, one from each shelf. Use this to find the probability that

a) both books are storybooks
b) both are textbooks.

9. The four aces and the four kings are removed from an ordinary pack of playing cards. One card is taken from the set of four aces and one card is taken from the set of four kings. Make a possibility space for the possible combinations of two cards and use it to find the probability that the two cards

a) are both black
b) are both spades
c) include at least one black card
d) are both of the same suit.

10 FORMULAE

Suppose that the lengths of the three sides of a triangle are a cm, b cm and c cm.

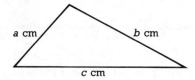

We find the perimeter of the triangle by adding these three lengths together.

If the perimeter is p cm, then

$$p = a + b + c$$

This is a formula for the perimeter of any triangle. When we know the values of a, b and c we can use the formula to work out the perimeter of that triangle.

USING A FORMULA

If we are given a formula $C = 2x + y$ and the values of x and y, we can use the formula to find the value of C

e.g., if $\qquad\qquad x = 3$ and $y = 4$

then $\qquad\qquad C = (2 \times 3) + 4$

$\qquad\qquad\qquad\quad = 6 + 4$

$\qquad\qquad\qquad\quad = 10$

We do not need to know what quantities the letters stand for to use the formula, but we do need to know the numbers.

119

EXERCISE 10a

If $x = y + 3$, find x when $y = 6$

$$y = 6$$
$$x = y + 3$$
$$= 6 + 3$$
$$= 9$$

1. If $t = 3 + p$, find t when $p = 7$

2. If $a = b - 3$, find a when $b = 9$

3. If $g = h + 6$, find g when $h = 8$

4. If $x = 7 - y$, find x when $y = 3$

If $C = a - p$, find C when $a = 10$ and $p = 6$

$$a = 10 \text{ and } p = 6$$
$$C = a - p$$
$$= 10 - 6$$
$$= 4$$

5. If $t = p + q$, find t when $p = 7$ and $q = 8$

6. If $a = b + c$, find a when $b = 10$ and $c = 9$

7. If $k = l - m$, find k when $l = 12$ and $m = 4$

8. If $z = y - x$, find z when $x = 3$ and $y = 11$

9. If $s = t + u$, find s when
   a) $t = 3$ and $u = 13$
   b) $t = 31$ and $u = 46$
   c) $t = 3.4$ and $u = 4.8$

10. If $q = p - r$, find q when
   a) $p = 19$ and $r = 5$
   b) $p = 13.4$ and $r = 2.2$
   c) $p = 6.8$ and $r = 5.84$

If $p = qr + 2$ find p when $q = 6$ and $r = 2$

$$q = 6, \ r = 2$$
$$p = qr + 2$$
$$= (6 \times 2) + 2$$
$$= 12 + 2$$
$$= 14$$

---

11. If $x = 4 + 3y$, find x when $y = 4$

12. If $a = 2b + c$, find a when $b = 5$ and $c = 6$

13. If $p = 5q - r$, find p when $q = 6$ and $r = 11$

14. If $a = bc + 7$, find a when $b = 4$ and $c = 2$

15. If $c = 6 + de$, find c when $d = 7$ and $e = 3$

16. If $x = yz - 2$, find x when $y = 3$ and $z = 4$

17. If $p = qr - 5$, find p when $q = 5$ and $r = 3$

18. The formula for working out the perimeter of a triangle is

$$p = a + b + c$$

where a units, b units and c units are the lengths of the sides and p units is the length of the perimeter. (All lengths must be given in the same unit.)

a) Find p when $a = 3$, $b = 2.7$ and $c = 4.2$

b) The lengths of the three sides of a triangle are 3 cm, 4 cm and 5 cm. Copy and complete this statement:
  $a =$, $b =$ and $c =$

c) With the values found in (b) use the formula to find the value of p.

d) What is the perimeter of the triangle given in (b)?

e) The lengths of the sides of another triangle are 15 mm, 3 cm and 25 mm. What values could you use for a, b and c in the formula for this triangle?

19. The cost of taking some people on an outing is given by the formula

$$C = 5n + 40t$$

where £C is the total cost, n is the number of people going and t is the number of coaches that are hired.

a) Find C when $n = 60$ and $t = 2$.

b) When 120 people go on the outing, 4 coaches are needed. Copy and complete this statement:
  $n =$, $t =$
  Now use the formula to find the cost in this case.

20. The formula $D = vt$ can be used to find the distance travelled by a train moving at constant speed; D is the number of kilometres travelled and t is the number of hours for which the train moves at v km/h.

a) The train travels at 55 km/h for $3\frac{1}{2}$ hours. Copy and complete this statement: $v =$ and $t =$

b) Now use the formula and the values for v and t from part (a) to find D.

c) Find the distance travelled by the train when it travels at 84 km/h for 1.75 hours.

In each question from 21 to 25 several alternative answers are given. Write down the letter that corresponds to the correct answer.

21. If $y = 5 + xz$, $x = 3$ and $z = 4$, then y is

    A 12   **B** 60   **C** 17   **D** 32

22. If $a = 6b + 7c$, $b = 3$ and $c = 2$, then a is

    A 13   **B** 33   **C** 18   **D** 32

23. If $p = qr - 3$, $q = 7$ and $r = 2$, then p is

    A 11   **B** 17   **C** 6   **D** 12

24. If $s = \frac{1}{2}(a + b + c)$, $a = 5$, $b = 7$ and $c = 6$, then s is

    A 18   **B** 9   **C** 36   **D** 105

25. If $d = ab + c$, $a = 3$, $b = 4$ and $c = 5$, then d is

    A 17   **B** 27   **C** 12   **D** 60

EXERCISE 10b

If $s = t(u - v)$ find s when $t = 3$, $u = 6$ and $v = 2$

$$t = 3, \ u = 6, \ v = 2$$
$$s = t(u - v)$$
$$= 3(6 - 2)$$
$$= 3 \times 4$$
$$= 12$$

1. If $x = 2(4 - y)$, find x when $y = 1$

2. If $p = q(6 + r)$, find p when $q = 3$ and $r = 2$

3. If $a = 3(5 - b)$, find a when $b = 3$

4. If $g = h(l + k)$, find g when $h = 7$, $l = 4$ and $k = 3$

5. If $H = h(5 + j)$, find H when $h = 3$ and $j = 7$

If $x = 4y^2$, find x when $y = 3$

$$y = 3$$
$$x = 4y^2$$
$$= 4 \times y \times y$$
$$= 4 \times 3 \times 3$$
$$= 36$$

6. If $p = q^2$, find p when $q = 6$

7. If $a = 6c^2$, find a when $c = 3$

8. If $x = 2 + y^2$, find x when $y = 4$

9. If $g = 5h^2$, find g when $h = 3$

10. If $x = yz^2$, find x when $y = 2$ and $z = 3$

11. If $y = x^2z$, find y when $x = 3$ and $z = 2$

If $p = \dfrac{q}{r - s}$, find p when $q = 24$, $r = 10$ and $s = 6$

$$q = 24, \ r = 10, \ s = 6$$
$$p = \frac{q}{r - s}$$
$$= \frac{24}{10 - 6}$$
$$= \frac{24}{4}$$
$$= 6$$

12. If $a = \dfrac{b+c}{3}$, find a when $b = 4$ and $c = 5$

13. If $p = \dfrac{4+q}{3+r}$, find p when $q = 8$ and $r = 1$

14. If $z = \dfrac{12-x}{y}$, find z when $x = 3$ and $y = 3$

15. If $p = \dfrac{2m}{n+3}$, find p when $m = 1$ and $n = 4$

16. If $x = 3y^2$, find x when $y = 7$

17. If $p = qr - 7$, find p when $q = 3$ and $r = 4$

18. If $g = \dfrac{h}{i+4}$, find g when $h = 6$ and $i = 8$

19. If $x = 6(y + z)$, find x when $y = 3$ and $z = 1$

Use the following information to answer questions 20 to 22.

The formula for the area of a square is $A = b^2$, where A is the number of units of area and b is the number of units of length of one side.

20. If the length of a side of a square is 2 cm, what is
a) the value of b c) the area of the square?
b) the value of A

21. The side of a square is 12 mm long. What is
a) the value of b c) the area of the square?
b) the value of A

22. When the length of a side of a square is 1.5 m, write down
a) the value of b c) the area of the square.
b) the value of A

23. A room is l m long, b m wide and h m high.
The area, A m^2, of the walls is given by the formula
$A = 2h(l + b)$
A room is 6 m long, 3 m wide and 3 m high.

a) Give the values of l, b and h.
b) Use the formula to find the area of the walls of the room.

24. The length, l cm, of a rectangle whose area is A cm^2, and
whose width is w cm, is given by the formula $l = \dfrac{A}{w}$
A rectangle is of area 36 cm^2 and its width is 3.6 cm.
Find its length in cm.

25. The cost, C pence, of x newspapers and y magazines is given
by the formula $C = 40x + 70y$.
Use the formula to find the cost of 4 newspapers and 3
magazines.

This formula can be used to work out the mechanical advantage of
a machine for lifting loads: $\mathscr{M} = \dfrac{L}{E}$

where $\mathscr{M}$ is a number called the mechanical advantage, the weight of
the load being lifted is L Newtons (force units) and the effort
needed to lift the load is E Newtons.

Use this information in questions 26 to 28.

26. A pulley system needs an effort of 25 Newtons to lift a load of
80 Newtons.

a) What is the value of L and of E ?
b) What is the value of $\mathscr{M}$?

27. A lever will lift a load of 40 Newtons for an effort of 15
Newtons.

a) Write down the values of L and E.
b) Use the formula to find the mechanical advantage of the
lever.

28. A hoist on a building site will lift a load of 500 Newtons when
the effort applied is 40 Newtons. Use the formula to find the
mechanical advantage of the hoist.

In each question from 29 to 31, several alternative answers are given. Write down the letter corresponding to the correct answer.

29. If $z = xy + 4$, $x = 6$ and $y = 7$, then z is

     A 38   **B** 46   **C** 17   **D** 66

30. If $a = \dfrac{b+c}{2}$, $b = 6$ and $c = 4$, then a is

     A 7   **B** 5   **C** 10   **D** $\frac{1}{5}$

31. If $p = q(4 - r)$, $q = 6$ and $r = 2$, then p is

     A 22   **B** 36   **C** 8   **D** 12

FINDING THE VALUE OF A LETTER ON THE RIGHT-HAND SIDE

The formula for finding the perimeter of a triangle is $p = a + b + c$. Sometimes we know the values of p, a and b, and need to find the value of c. We can do this by putting the given numbers in their correct positions. This then gives an equation with one letter, which we can solve.

EXERCISE 10c

If $a = 2b + c$, find b when $a = 12$ and $c = 2$

$$a = 12, \ c = 2$$
$$a = 2b + c$$
$$12 = 2b + 2$$

Take 2 from each side $10 = 2b$

Divide both sides by 2 $5 = b$

i.e. $b = 5$

1. If $x = y + z$, find y when $x = 6$ and $z = 2$

2. If $p = q - r$, find q when $p = 3$ and $r = 4$

3. If $a = b + 2c$, find b when $a = 10$ and $c = 3$

4. If $x = 2y - z$, find z when $x = 12$ and $y = 8$

5. If $t = 3s + u$, find s when $t = 17$ and $u = 2$

If $p = qr + 1$, find q if $p = 5$ and $r = 2$

$$p = 5, \ r = 2$$
$$p = qr + 1$$
$$5 = q \times 2 + 1$$
i.e. $5 = 2q + 1$
Take 1 from each side $4 = 2q$
Divide both sides by 2 $2 = q$
i.e. $q = 2$

---

6. If $x = yz$, find z when $x = 10$ and $y = 5$

7. If $s = tu$, find t when $s = 16$ and $u = 8$

8. If $p = tu + 4$, find u when $p = 16$ and $t = 3$

9. If $a = bc - 3$, find c when $a = 11$ and $b = 2$

10. If $d = ef - 7$, find f when $d = 1$ and $e = 2$

MAKING FORMULAE ━━━━━━━━━━━━━━━━━━━━━━━━━━━━━━━━━━━━

We can use a flow chart to help make a formula.

EXERCISE 10d

Gemma is three years older than Ahmed.

a) Copy and complete this flow chart:

(Ahmed's age)━▶[ ]━▶(Gemma's age)

Use it to help answer (b) and (c).

b) When Ahmed is 10, how old is Gemma?

c) Write a formula for Gemma's age, y years, when Ahmed is x years old.

a)
(Ahmed's age)━▶[+3]━▶(Gemma's age)
10   13

b) Gemma is 13 years old.

c)
(Ahmed's age)━▶[+3]━▶(Gemma's age)
x y

[$x + 3$]

GEMMA'S AGE IS y
SO $y = x + 3$.

$y = x + 3$

---

1. The bus fare between the school and the station is 70 p.

a) Copy and complete this flow chart.

(Number of people)━▶[ ]━▶(Total cost)

b) What is the total cost for eight people making this journey?

c) Write down a formula for the cost, C pence, for n people making the journey.

2. One tube of sweets costs 25 p.

   a) Copy and complete this flow chart.

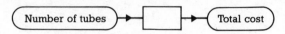

   b) What is the cost of six tubes of sweets?
   c) Write down a formula for the cost, C pence, of n tubes of sweets.

3. I think of a number and then subtract 4.

   a) Copy and complete this flow chart.

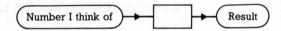

   b) If the number I think of is 56, what is the result?
   c) Write down a formula for the result, y, if the number I think of is x.

4. The cost of one cake is 24 p.

   a) Draw a flow chart to show how the cost of a number of cakes can be found.
   b) What is the total cost of six cakes?
   c) Write a formula for the total cost, C pence, of n cakes.

5. At the beginning of term, each pupil is given two exercise books.

   a) Draw a flow chart to show how the number of exercise books needed for several pupils can be found.
   b) How many books are needed for 75 pupils?
   c) Write a formula for the number of books, N, needed for n pupils.

6. The number of teaspoonfuls of tea needed can be found from the rule "one teaspoonful for each person plus one for the pot".

   a) How many teaspoonfuls are needed for four people?
   b) Write a formula for the number of teaspoonfuls, T, needed for n people.

7. The rule for cooking a casserole slowly is "one hour for each pound of meat plus one hour".

    a) For how long should a casserole with two pounds of meat in it be cooked?

    b) Write a formula for the number of hours, H, needed to cook a casserole made from n pounds of meat.

8. In an examination, each pupil is given two sheets of paper and ten sheets of paper are put on the teacher's desk.

    a) Copy and complete this flow chart.

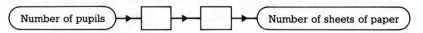

    b) How many sheets of paper are needed for a room with 15 pupils in it?

    c) Find a formula for the number of sheets of paper, N, needed for a room with n pupils in it.

9. This flow chart can be used to find the cost, C pence, of n tubes of paint that cost d pence each.

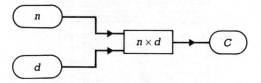

Notice that to start this flow chart we need to feed *two* numbers into it.

    a) Find the cost of ten tubes at 45 pence each.

    b) Find a formula for the cost, C pence, of n tubes at d pence each.

10. This flow chart needs *three* numbers fed into it to start it off. It can be used to find the mean value of the three numbers.

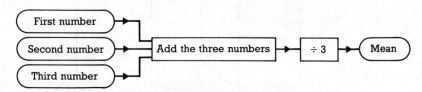

    a) Find the mean of the numbers 2, 6 and 7.

    b) Find a formula for finding the mean, m, of the numbers a, b and c.

11 PLANS AND ELEVATIONS

PLANS AND ELEVATIONS

An architect presents drawings of a building partly in picture form and partly as diagrams.

The drawings need to show a *plan* of each floor, that is, a diagram of what is seen when looking down.

They also show *elevations*, that is, side and front views of the building and sometimes the back view as well.

This is a simple example.

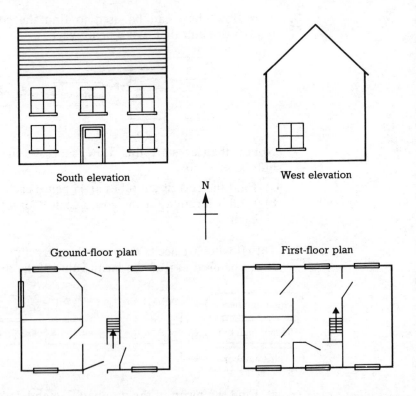

South elevation

West elevation

N

Ground-floor plan

First-floor plan

Notice that the heights of the two elevations agree and that the widths of the plans and elevations agree.

EXERCISE 11a 1. a) How many windows are there on the east side of the house on the previous page?

b) Would the east elevation be the same width as the west elevation or the same width as the south elevation?

c) Draw the east elevation of the house on the previous page. Make sure that it is the correct height and width.

2. Here is a drawing of a free-standing garage with one window. The rear elevation of the garage is also shown.

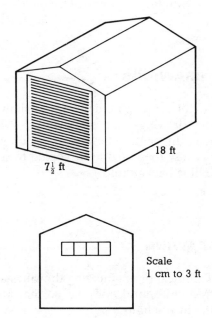

Scale
1 cm to 3 ft

a) Sketch the plan and mark in the measurements, then draw the plan accurately on squared paper.

b) Use the drawing of the rear elevation to find the total height of the garage and the height of the side wall.

c) Sketch and draw accurately a side elevation of the garage.

3.

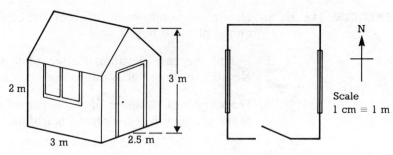

Above are a drawing of a garden shed and the plan of the floor of the shed.

a) Draw the south elevation of the shed.

b) Draw the west elevation of the shed.

Notice that there is no information about the heights of windows or doors. Decide for yourself what they should be.

ARCHITECTS' DRAWINGS

Architects prepare drawings to show to their clients. For the builders, the drawings are on a large scale and show every detail and measurement. (These working drawings are often called blueprints because they used to be copied by a method that gave white lines on a blue background.)

TECHNICAL DRAWING

Technical or engineering drawings are produced for the same reason as architectural ones, i.e. so that an object may be made exactly to the instructions.

Most drawings are now prepared on a computer using Computer Aided Design (CAD). They are very sophisticated and can show the view from any direction.

On the opposite page there is an example of a working drawing of a clamp. The drawing would probably be full-size but the measurements would be given as well.

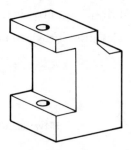

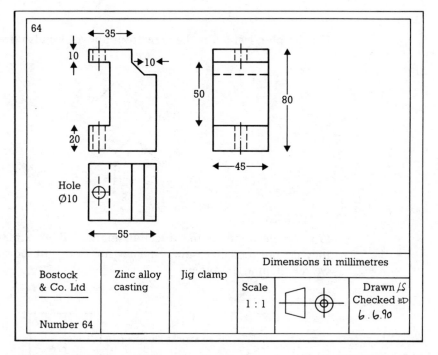

The person who prepares these drawings is called a draughtsman. There are rules for doing these drawings. In this chapter we will introduce a few of them.

If you look at a cube you will see something like this, which is a picture of the cube in perspective.

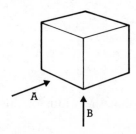

Technical drawings, however, are diagrams and not pictures.

For the elevation or view in the direction marked A we draw a square.

Elevation in direction A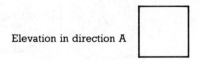

For the plan (which is the view from above) we also draw a square.

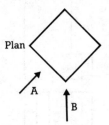

For the elevation in the direction marked B we see two sides but they do not look like squares. They are both foreshortened because we see them at an angle.

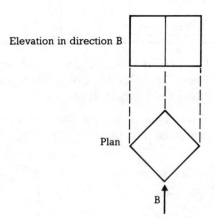

Notice that the width of this elevation is the same as that of the plan.

EXERCISE 11b

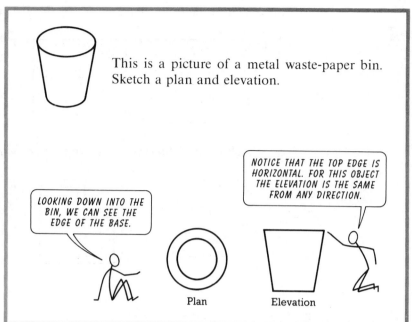

This is a picture of a metal waste-paper bin.
Sketch a plan and elevation.

NOTICE THAT THE TOP EDGE IS
HORIZONTAL. FOR THIS OBJECT
THE ELEVATION IS THE SAME
FROM ANY DIRECTION.

LOOKING DOWN INTO THE
BIN, WE CAN SEE THE
EDGE OF THE BASE.

Plan   Elevation

1.

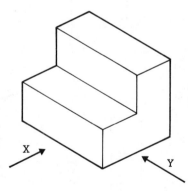

a) Which of the following diagrams is the plan of this object?

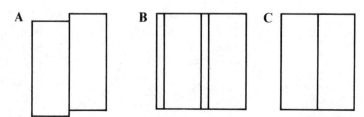

b) Which of the following diagrams is the elevation from X?

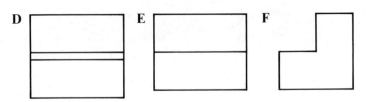

c) Which of the following drawings is the elevation from Y?

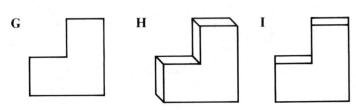

2.

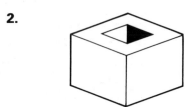

Sketch the plan of this object.

3.

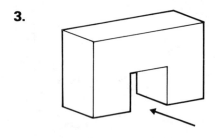

Sketch the elevation of this object in the direction of the arrow.

4.

a) Sketch a plan of this lampshade.
b) Sketch an elevation of the lampshade. Does it matter from which direction you choose to view it?

5.

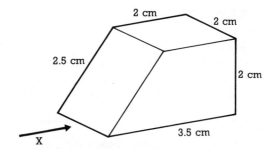

2 cm
2 cm
2.5 cm
2 cm
3.5 cm
X

a) Which of the following diagrams is the plan of this object?

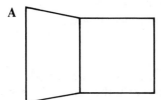

A

B

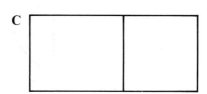

C

b) Which of the following diagrams is the elevation in the direction marked X?

D

E

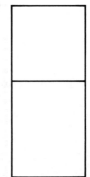

F

ACCURATE DRAWING

So far you have been asked only to sketch the plan and elevations of the objects. Now we are going to make accurate drawings.

EXERCISE 11c

This is a square-based pyramid.

a) Sketch the plan of the pyramid and mark in the known measurements.

b) Which given measurement have you not used?

c) Draw the plan accurately.

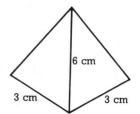

a) (Looking down from above, we see the edge of the square base with the top in the centre.)

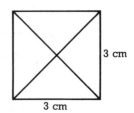

b) The length of the sloping edge, 6 cm, is not used.

c)

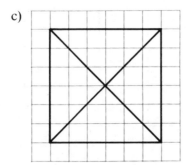

In each question, sketch the required diagrams and mark in any known measurements.
Then draw each diagram accurately on squared paper.

1.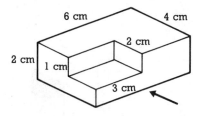

a) The plan.
b) The elevation in the direction of the arrow.

2.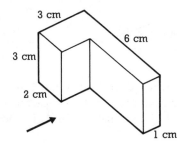

a) The plan.
b) The elevation in the direction of the arrow.

3. The height and depth of each step is 2 cm.

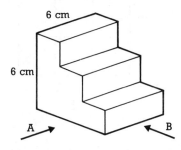

a) The plan.
b) The elevation in direction A.
c) The elevation in direction B.

4. The plan of a sphere of radius 3 cm.

5. This cylinder has a radius of 4 cm and a height of 6 cm.

a) The plan of the cylinder.
b) The elevation. (This is the same from any direction.)

HIDDEN LINES

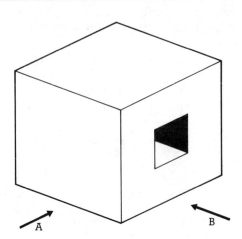

This cube has a hole through it. You might think that the plan of it is nothing more than a square, but to indicate the position of the hole we represent the hidden edges by broken lines.

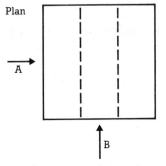

You can imagine that the object is made of clear plastic so that you see the hidden edges faintly.

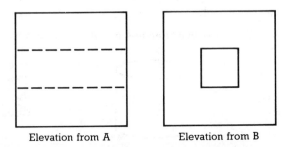

Elevation from A   Elevation from B

EXERCISE 11d In this exercise, use squared paper.

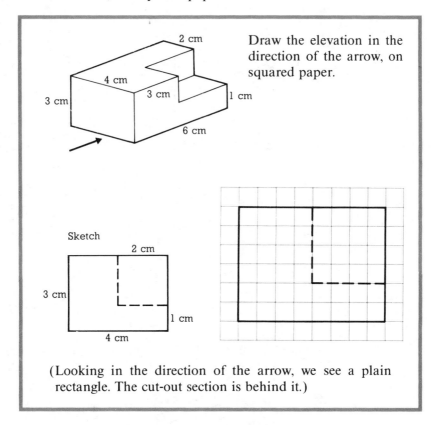

Draw the elevation in the direction of the arrow, on squared paper.

(Looking in the direction of the arrow, we see a plain rectangle. The cut-out section is behind it.)

In each question from 1 to 4, draw the plan.

1.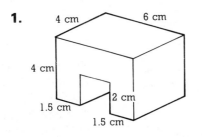

3.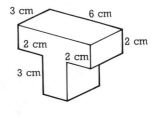

2.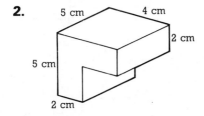

4.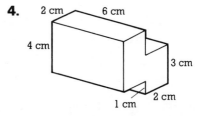

In each question from 5 to 8, draw the elevation in the direction of the arrow.

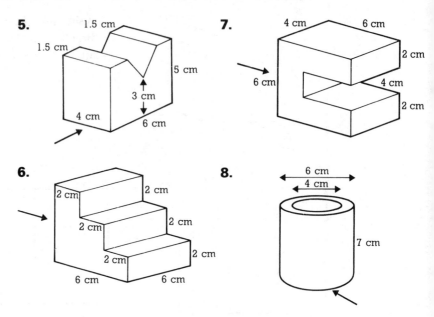

In questions 9 and 10 draw the plan and the elevations in the directions of the arrows.

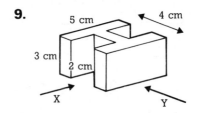

All the pieces have a thickness of 1 cm.

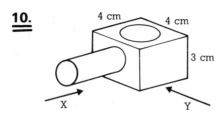

The hole, which goes right through this object, has a diameter of 3 cm.

The handle has a diameter of 2 cm. It is 4 cm long and is fixed to the centre of the face.

12 SPEED AND OTHER COMPOUND UNITS

If a car is driven at a steady speed and covers 40 miles in 1 hour then we say its speed is 40 miles per hour or 40 mph.

EXERCISE 12a

> A car covers 55 miles in 1 hour. What is its speed?
>
> The car's speed is 55 mph.

Give the speeds in the following cases, assuming that the speeds are steady.

1. A man walks 4 miles in 1 hour.

2. A cyclist covers 10 miles in 1 hour.

3. A motorist covers 32 miles in 1 hour.

4. A plane flies 250 miles in 1 hour.

5. Concorde flies 1250 miles in 1 hour.

6. A motorcyclist covers 55 miles in 1 hour.

We can use other units. A speed of 10 kilometres per hour is written 10 km/h. A speed of 5 metres per second is written 5 m/s.

Give the speeds in the following cases.

7. A bird flies 2 m in 1 second.

8. A cyclist travels 6 m in 1 second.

145

9. A motorist drives 45 km in 1 hour.

10. A plane flies 1020 km in 1 hour.

11. A snail moves 2 m in 1 hour.

12. A cheetah runs 30 m in 1 second.

CALCULATING SPEED

If a car covers 70 miles in 2 hours at a steady speed, it covers 35 miles in 1 hour, so its speed is 35 mph.

To find the speed we divide the distance travelled by the time taken,

i.e.

$$\text{Speed} = \frac{\text{distance}}{\text{time}}$$

EXERCISE 12b

At a steady speed, a cyclist covers 60 km in 4 hours. What is her speed?

$$\text{Steady speed} = \frac{\text{distance}}{\text{time}}$$

$$= \frac{60}{4} \text{ km/h}$$

$$= 15 \text{ km/h}$$

Find the steady speeds in the following cases.

1. A man walks 12 km in 3 hours.

2. A cyclist travels 22 miles in 2 hours.

3. A motorist drives 126 miles in 3 hours.

4. A plane flies 1250 miles in 5 hours.

5. A motorcyclist travels 196 km in 2 hours.

6. A deer runs 36 m in 8 seconds.

In questions 7 to 10, several alternative answers are given. Write down the letter that corresponds to the correct answer.

7. At a steady speed, a walker covers 20 km in 4 hours. His speed is

A 5 km/h   **B** 4 km/h   **C** 20 km/h   **D** $\frac{1}{5}$ km/h

8. At a steady speed, a motorboat travels 76 km in 4 hours. Its speed is

A $\frac{1}{19}$ km/h   **B** 19 mph   **C** 76 km/h   **D** 19 km/h

9. At a steady speed, a marble rolls 15 m in 5 seconds. Its speed is

A 15 m/s   **B** 5 m/s   **C** $\frac{1}{3}$ m/s   **D** 3 m/s

10. At a steady speed, a runner covers 120 m in 12 seconds. His speed is

A 120 m/s   **B** 12 m/s   **C** 12 mph   **D** 10 m/s

Sometimes the time is not an exact number of hours or seconds.

At a steady speed, a cyclist travels 27 km in $2\frac{1}{4}$ hours. What is the speed?

$$\text{Time} = 2\frac{1}{4} \text{ hours} = 2.25 \text{ h}$$

$$\text{Steady speed} = \frac{\text{distance}}{\text{time}}$$

$$= \frac{27}{2.25} \text{ km/h}$$

$$= 12 \text{ km/h}$$

Find the speeds in the following cases, assuming that they are steady.

11.   A motorist travels 63 km in $1\frac{1}{2}$ hours.

12.   A walker covers 3 miles in $\frac{3}{4}$ hour.

13.   A cyclist travels 21 km in 1 hour 45 minutes.

14.   A plane flies 243 miles in $1\frac{1}{2}$ hours.

15.   A train travels 200 miles in $2\frac{1}{2}$ hours.

16.   A runner covers 100 m in $12\frac{1}{2}$ seconds.

17.   A dog walks 21 m in $7\frac{1}{2}$ seconds.

AVERAGE SPEED

Suppose that we travel by bus, from one town to another 40 miles away, taking 2 hours.

At times the bus travels quickly, at other times slowly and sometimes, at traffic lights or at road junctions, it does not move at all.

The speed changes all the time; it is not a steady speed.

If we can imagine doing the same journey of 40 miles at a steady speed, and taking the same time, then the speed would be $\frac{40}{2}$ mph i.e. 20 mph.

This imaginary speed is called the average speed, or the mean speed.

$$\text{Average speed} = \frac{\text{total distance}}{\text{total time}}$$

EXERCISE 12c

> A car travels 60 km in a time of $1\frac{1}{2}$ hours. What is its average speed?
>
> $$\text{Time} = 1\frac{1}{2} \text{ hours} = 1.5 \text{ h}$$
>
> $$\text{Average speed} = \frac{\text{total distance}}{\text{total time}}$$
>
> $$= \frac{60}{1.5} \text{ km/h}$$
>
> $$= 40 \text{ km/h}$$

Find the average speeds in the following cases.

1. A cyclist travels 19 km in 2 hours.

2. A walker covers 9 miles in 3 hours.

3. A train travels 360 km in 4 hours.

4. A runner covers 1000 m in 200 seconds.

5. A motorist drives 48 miles in $1\frac{1}{2}$ hours.

6. A plane flies 1750 km in $2\frac{1}{2}$ hours.

7. A motorboat covers 15 km in $\frac{3}{4}$ hour.

8. A motorcyclist travels 90 km in $1\frac{1}{2}$ hours.

9. A marathon runner covers 26 miles in 4 hours.

10. A bullet moves 60 m in $\frac{1}{2}$ second.

11. A ball moves 35 m in $1\frac{1}{4}$ seconds.

12. A racing car covers 3 miles in $\frac{1}{60}$ hour.

DISTANCE AND TIME

If a car travels at an average speed of 30 mph for 4 hours then it will travel 30 × 4 miles, i.e. 120 miles, in the 4 hours.

> Distance = average speed × time
>
> $$\text{Time} = \frac{\text{distance}}{\text{average speed}}$$

This diagram helps us to remember the relationships between speed (*S*), distance (*D*) and time (*T*).

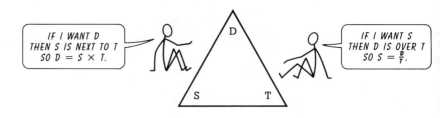

EXERCISE 12d

A cyclist travels at an average speed of 10 mph for 2 hours. How far does he go?

Distance = average speed × time

= 10 × 2 miles

= 20 miles

Find the distances travelled in the following cases.

1. A car is driven at an average speed of 40 mph, for 3 hours.

2. A yacht sails at an average speed of 8 km/h for 5 hours.

3. A cyclist rides at an average speed of 7.5 mph for 2 hours.

4. A plane flies at an average speed of 1250 km/h for $5\frac{1}{2}$ hours.

5. A swimmer swims at an average speed of 2.2 m/s for 13.5 seconds.

A plane flies 800 km at an average speed of 150 km/h. How many minutes does it take?

$$\text{Time} = \frac{\text{distance}}{\text{average speed}}$$

(The speed is in kilometres per hour so the time will be in hours.)

$$= \frac{800}{150} \text{ hours}$$

$$= 5.33 \ldots \text{ hours}$$

$$= 5.33 \ldots \times 60 \text{ minutes}$$

$$= 320 \text{ minutes}$$

Find the times taken in the following cases. Give your answers in hours, in minutes, or in seconds as appropriate.

6. A car is driven 125 km at an average speed of 75 km/h.

7. A wheelbarrow is pushed along at an average speed of 0.6 m/s over a distance of 33 m.

8. A heavy load is being transported a distance of 147 km at an average speed of 10.5 km/h.

9. A bicycle is ridden at an average speed of 18 km/h over a distance of 45 km.

10. A glider travels 93 km at an average speed of 15 km/h.

11. Merton and Caxton are 63 km apart. Mr Abel takes $1\frac{3}{4}$ hours to drive from one to the other. What is his average speed?

12. During the night, a badger moves through a wood for 5 hours. Its average speed is 1.5 km/h. What distance does it cover?

13. In the eighteenth century, the mail coach from London to Bristol travelled 119 miles at an average speed of 7 mph. How long did the journey take?

14. A hot-air balloon floats, carried along by the wind. It is in the air for $4\frac{1}{2}$ hours and travels at an average speed of 1.5 km/h. What distance does it travel?

15. The speed of sound is 330 m/s. How many seconds does the noise of an explosion take to travel 825 m?

A plane flies at an average speed of 250 km/h for 45 minutes. How far does it fly?

(The speed is given in kilometres per *hour* and the time is given in *minutes*. The units of time must be the same, so we will change 45 minutes to hours.)

$$\text{Time} = \frac{45}{60} \text{ hours}$$
$$= 0.75 \text{ hours}$$

$$\text{Distance} = \text{average speed} \times \text{time}$$
$$= 250 \times 0.75 \text{ km}$$
$$= 187.5 \text{ km}$$

Find the distances travelled in the following cases.

16. An inter-city train is driven at an average speed of 125 mph for 84 minutes.

17. A girl jogs for 20 minutes at an average speed of 12 km/h.

18. A motorcyclist rides for 12 minutes at an average speed of 70 mph.

19. A car is driven at 55 km/h for 36 minutes.

20. A speedboat travels at 24 km/h for 1 hour 10 minutes.

COMPOUND UNITS

Three basic quantities that we meet in everyday life are length, time and mass. (The word weight is often used when we mean mass but you know from your science courses that weight really means something different.)

Other quantities can be expressed in terms of length, mass and time and are measured in compound units, i.e. units that are combinations of mass, length and time units.

For example, a speed of 100 km/h involves both kilometres and hours, i.e. a unit of speed is a compound unit formed from the units of distance and time.

The units for area and volume are also compound units. For example, a volume of 12 cm^3 involves a set of three distance units.

CAPACITY

A particular type of volume is called capacity.

The word capacity is usually used to describe the volume that can be put into a container designed to hold liquids such as a jug, a bottle or a water tank.

The basic unit of capacity is the litre where

$$1 \text{ litre} = 1000 \text{ cm}^3$$

The volume of a liquid is usually given in litres rather than in cubic centimetres. For example we talk about 1 litre of milk rather than 1000 cm^3 of milk.

EXERCISE 12e

Express 5.6 litres in cubic centimetres.

$$1 \text{ litre } = 1000 \text{ cm}^3$$

so $\qquad$ 5.6 litres $= 5.6 \times 1000 \text{ cm}^3$

$$= 5600 \text{ cm}^3$$

Express in cm^3

1. 3.4 litres $\qquad$ **3.** 0.25 litres $\qquad$ **5.** 0.005 litres

2. 2.65 litres $\qquad$ **4.** 14 litres $\qquad$ **6.** 0.073 litres

Express in litres

7. 4000 cm^3 $\qquad$ **9.** 800 cm^3 $\qquad$ **11.** 7000 cm^3

8. 8000 cm^3 $\qquad$ **10.** 43 000 cm^3 $\qquad$ **12.** 500 cm^3

Small quantities of liquid are measured in millilitres (mℓ) where

$$1 \text{ litre } = 1000 \text{ m}\ell$$

Now 1 litre $= 1000 \text{ cm}^3$ so $1 \text{ m}\ell = 1 \text{ cm}^3$.

Express each quantity in the unit given in brackets.

13. 500 ml (cm^3) $\qquad$ **16.** 2500 cm^3 (litres)

14. 1.5 litres (mℓ) $\qquad$ **17.** 250 cm^3 (mℓ)

15. 300 cm^3 (mℓ) $\qquad$ **18.** 5 litres (cm^3)

We will now look at some other quantities that are measured in compound units.

COVERAGE

The coverage of paint, fertilizer, spray etc. tells us about the amount used and the area it covers.

If a lot of liquid is needed to cover an area, coverage is given as the quantity of liquid per unit of area, e.g. litres per square metre (ℓ/m^2).

EXERCISE 12f

A lawn weedkiller should be applied with a coverage of 25 g/m². What area of lawn should a packet containing 500 g of weedkiller cover?

(25 g/m² means that one square metre needs 25 g of weedkiller.)

500 g should cover $500 \div 25 \text{ m}^2$

$= 20 \text{ m}^2$

1. It is recommended that the amount of fertiliser that should be used is 50 g/m².

   a) How many grams of fertiliser are needed to cover an area of one square metre?

   b) How many grams of fertiliser are needed to cover an area of 100 m²?

   c) What area will 200 g of fertiliser cover?

2. Asphalt is applied with a coverage of 20 kg/m².

   a) How many kilograms of asphalt are needed to cover an area of one square metre?

   b) How many kilograms are needed to cover a drive with an area of 100 m²?

   c) What area will be 1000 kg of asphalt cover?

If only a little liquid is needed, coverage is given as the area covered by one unit of liquid, e.g. square metres per litre (m^2/ℓ).

The coverage of *Gold Star* floor varnish is given as $10\ m^2/\ell$ on bare wood. What area of bare wood should a tin holding $5\ \ell$ of varnish cover?

($10\ m^2/\ell$ means that one litre covers an area of $10\ m^2$.)

$5\ \ell$ should cover $\quad 5 \times 10\ m^2$

$\qquad\qquad\qquad = 50\ m^2$

---

3. The instructions on a tin of gloss paint state that the contents have a coverage of $10\ m^2/\ell$.

    a) What area will one litre of this paint cover?

    b) The tin contains two litres of paint. What area should this cover?

    c) Freda buys a half litre tin of this paint. What area can she expect to cover?

4. Five litres of varnish cover an area of $30\ m^2$.

    a) What area would one litre cover?

    b) What is the coverage in terms of m^2/ℓ?

Look carefully at the units given for each remaining question and decide what they mean.

5. Insecticide spray is applied with a coverage of $4\ m^2/\ell$. What area will 5 litres cover?

6. It is recommended that bitumen should be applied with a coverage of $150\ g/m^2$ to seal a flat roof. What weight of bitumen is needed to seal a flat roof with an area of $25.4\ m^2$?

7. Gravel to cover a path should be applied with a coverage of $20\ kg/m^2$.

    a) How much gravel is needed to cover a path with an area of $150\ m^2$?

    b) What area of the path will 500 kg of gravel cover?

8. An emulsion paint should cover at about 12 m²/ℓ. How much paint is needed to cover 150 m² of wall surface?

9. Concentrated orange squash should be diluted to a strength of 40 mℓ/ℓ.
    a) How much concentrated orange squash should be used in one litre of water?
    b) How much concentrated squash is needed for 10 litres of water?
    c) What quantity of water is needed to dilute 500 mℓ of squash?

10. The instructions on a packet of wallpaper adhesive state that it should be mixed with water in the proportion of 50 g/ℓ, and that one litre of made-up paste is sufficient for two standard rolls of wallpaper.
    There are 125 g left in my packet of adhesive. How many rolls of wallpaper can I hang with this amount?

DENSITY

The density of a material is the mass of one unit of volume. For example, if a block of wood has a mass of 20 kg and a volume of 2 m³ then it has a mass of 10 kg for each cubic metre. So the density of the wood is 10 kg/m³.

$$\text{Density} = \frac{\text{mass}}{\text{volume}}$$

EXERCISE 12g

A piece of metal weighs 100 g and its volume is 16 cm³. What is the density of the metal?

$$\text{Density} = \frac{\text{mass}}{\text{volume}}$$

$$= \frac{100}{16} \text{ g/cm}^3$$

$$= 6.25 \text{ g/cm}^3$$

Find the density of the material from which each of the following objects is made.

1. A brick with a mass of 1000 g and a volume of 800 cm^3.

2. A wood block with a mass of 420 g and a volume of 500 cm^3.

3. A stone step with a mass of 200 kg and a volume of 1.5 m^3.

4. A bar of lead with a mass of 2850 g and a volume of 250 cm^3.

5. An ingot of pure gold with a mass of 5720 g and a volume of 300 cm^3.

6. A container of detergent holds 3000 cm^3 of liquid which has a mass of 3.3 kg.
   a) What is the mass of the liquid in grams?
   b) What is the density of the liquid in g/cm^3?

7. A panel of glass has a mass of 1 kg and a volume of 400 cm^3.
   a) What is the mass of the panel in grams?
   b) What is the density of the glass?

8. The density of sea water is 1.05 g/cm^3.
   a) What is the mass of 1000 cm^3 of sea water?
   b) A bucket is filled with sea water. The capacity of the bucket is 4000 cm^3. What is the mass of the water in the bucket?

9. Oak has a density of 800 kg/m^3. A table made from oak has a mass of 200 kg. What is the volume of wood in the table?

10. A rectangular sheet of balsa wood measures 100 cm by 50 cm and it is 0.2 cm thick.
    a) What is the volume of the piece of balsa wood?
    b) The sheet was weighed and found to have a mass of 200 g. What is the density of balsa wood?

11. The density of some liquid detergent is 1.05 g/cm^3.
    a) What is the mass of 4 cm^3 of this liquid?
    b) What is the volume of 20 g of this liquid?

12. The density of cork is 0.25 g/cm^3. Find the volume of a piece of cork which weighs 100 g.

13. The density of aluminium foil is 2.7 g/cm³. A sheet of this foil is 1 m long, 30 cm wide and 0.01 cm thick. How much does it weigh?

14. A sky-light has an area of 15 000 cm². It is covered with glass which is 5 mm thick. The density of the glass is 2.5 g/cm³. What is the weight of the sky-light?

FUEL CONSUMPTION

Fuel consumption is the rate at which fuel is used. There is no standard way of giving fuel consumption; it depends on what is using the fuel and what the fuel is.

A car uses petrol, and its petrol consumption is given either as the number of miles travelled on one gallon of petrol, i.e. miles per gallon (mpg), or as the number of litres used to travel 100 kilometres, i.e. litres per 100 km (ℓ/100 km).

When vast quantities of fuel are used, e.g. in rockets, the consumption is given as the quantity of fuel used in one unit of time or to cover one unit of distance.

For example, the coal consumption of a power station could be given as the number of tons of coal used per hour and the fuel consumption of a rocket could be given as litres per second.

Look carefully at the units used to describe fuel consumption.

EXERCISE 12h 1. A car uses fuel at the rate of 40 mpg. How far can it be expected to go on five gallons of petrol?

2. A plane uses fuel at the rate of 10 ℓ/km when cruising at a steady speed. How many litres of fuel does it need to fly 300 km at this speed?

3. A coal-burning power station uses coal at the rate of 200 tons/hour. How many hours will 8000 tons of coal last?

4. The first stage of a rocket uses up fuel at the rate of 100 ℓ/s. It starts with 6000 ℓ of fuel. For how many seconds does it burn before it runs out of fuel?

5. A car uses petrol at the rate of 20 ℓ/100 km. How much petrol will it use for a journey of 300 km?

6. A lorry uses diesel at the rate of 2 km/ℓ. How many kilometres is it likely to travel on 100 litres of diesel?

7. A rocket uses fuel at the rate of 20 ℓ/s. Simon wants to know how far it will travel on 100 ℓ of fuel. If you can answer Simon's question do so; if you cannot, say briefly why not.

8. A Boeing 747 engine uses fuel at the rate of 2400 lb/hour in steady flight and at ten times this rate when taking off and climbing. A 747 plane (which has four engines) takes 3 minutes to take off and climb to its cruising height. What mass of fuel does it use during this time?

13 QUADRILATERALS, POLYGONS AND TESSELLATIONS

QUADRILATERALS

In Book 2B we saw that the sum of the angles of a triangle is 180°. Provided that the sides that come together are of equal length we can place two triangles together to form a quadrilateral.

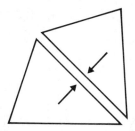 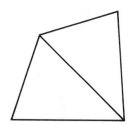

It follows that the sum of the four angles of a quadrilateral is 360°.

Every quadrilateral can be divided into two triangles by cutting it along a diagonal.

Therefore,

> the sum of the interior angles of any quadrilateral is 360°

EXERCISE 13a

Find the size of the marked angle.

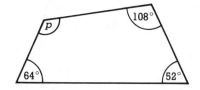

$$p + 108° + 52° + 64° = 360°$$
$$p + 224° = 360°$$
$$p = 136°$$

In questions 1 to 8 find the size of each marked angle.

1.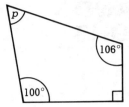

5.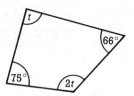

2.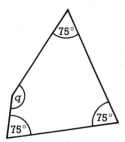

6.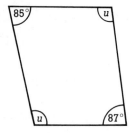

3.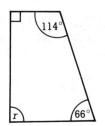

7.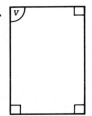

4.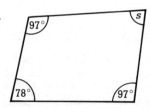

8.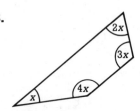

SQUARES AND RECTANGLES

EXERCISE 13b 1. What shape do you see when you look at each of the objects shown in the diagrams?

a)

e)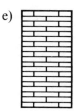

b)

f)

c)

g)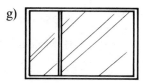

d)

h)

2. What shape is

a) the door to your classroom

b) the blackboard

c) the floor tiles

d) the ceiling tiles

e) a page from your textbook

f) the window of the room you are in

g) the flat surface on which you are writing?

3. Name some everyday objects whose outline shapes are (a) squares (b) rectangles.

4.

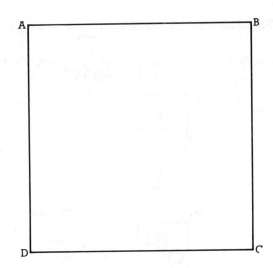

Look at the quadrilateral ABCD.

a) Measure the sides of the quadrilateral.

b) Measure the angles A, B, C and D.

c) Are any of the sides equal? If so, name them.

d) Are any of the sides parallel? If so, name them.

e) What is the special name of this quadrilateral?

5. Repeat question 4 for the quadrilateral below.

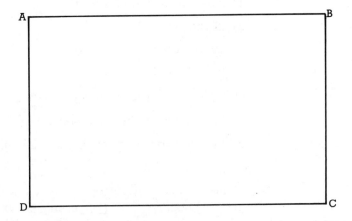

SQUARE

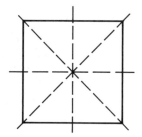

A square has four lines of symmetry.

All four sides of a square are equal and all four angles are right angles.

RECTANGLE

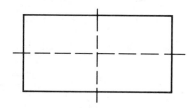

A rectangle has two lines of symmetry.

The opposite sides of a rectangle are equal and all four angles are right angles.

OTHER SPECIAL QUADRILATERALS

PARALLELOGRAM

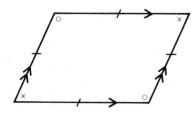

A parallelogram has no lines of symmetry but it does have rotational symmetry of order 2.

The opposite sides are equal and parallel.

The opposite angles are equal.

RHOMBUS

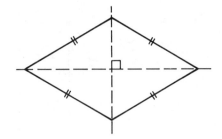

The two diagonals of a rhombus are lines of symmetry.

A rhombus has rotational symmetry of order 2.

The opposite angles are equal.

The opposite sides are parallel.

All four sides are the same length.

The diagonals cut at right angles.

KITE

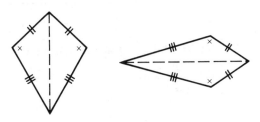

A kite has one line of symmetry. It has no rotational symmetry.

A kite has one pair of opposite angles equal and two pairs of adjacent sides equal.

TRAPEZIUM

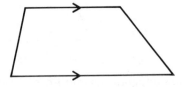

A trapezium usually has no symmetry.

It has one pair of parallel sides.

EXERCISE 13c For each question from 1 to 4, measure all four sides of the quadrilateral. Then answer the following questions:

    a) Are any of the sides equal? If so, name them.
    b) What special name do we give to this quadrilateral?

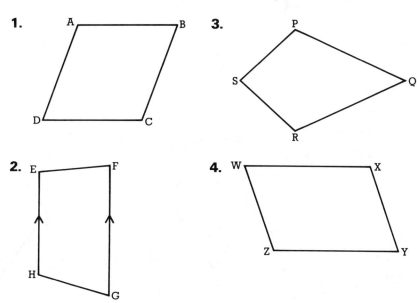

EXERCISE 13d State whether each of the following quadrilaterals is a square, a rectangle, a rhombus, a kite or a trapezium. If it is none of these, write "general quadrilateral".

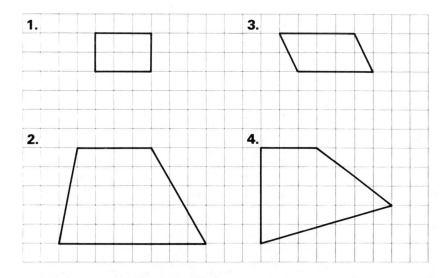

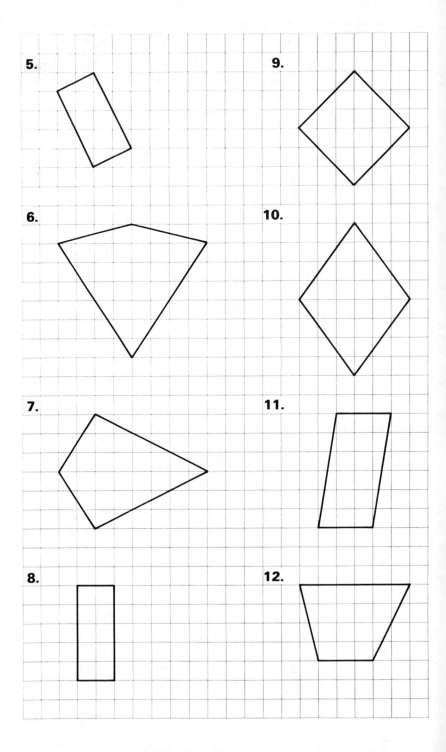

5.

6.

7.

8.

9.

10.

11.

12.

FINDING ANGLES IN QUADRILATERALS ▬▬▬▬▬▬▬▬▬▬▬▬▬▬

EXERCISE 13e

a) Identify the quadrilateral.

b) Find the sizes of the marked angles.

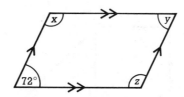

a) This is a parallelogram.

b) $x + 72° = 180°$ (interior angles)

$x = 108°$

$y = 72°$ (opposite angles of a parallelogram)

$z = x = 108°$ (opposite angles of a parallelogram)

In each question from 1 to 4   a) name the type of quadrilateral

b) give reasons for your answer to (a)

c) find the sizes of the marked angles.

1.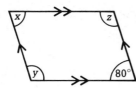

3.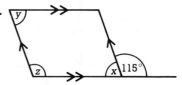

2.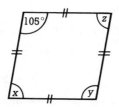

4.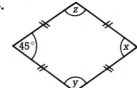

In each question from 5 to 8 there is more than one type of quadrilateral.

a) Name each different type of quadrilateral that you find.

b) Find the sizes of the marked angles.

5.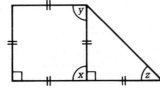

7.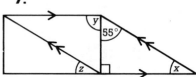

6.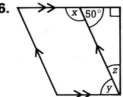

8.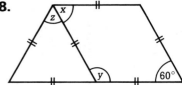

ABCD is a kite. Find the sizes of the marked angles.

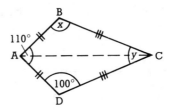

$x = 100°$ (AC is a line of symmetry)

The four angles of a quadrilateral add up to 360°

so $110° + 100° + y + 100° = 360°$

i.e. $y + 310° = 360°$

$y = 50°$

Find the sizes of the marked angles

9.

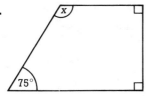

13.

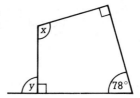

10.

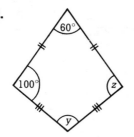

14.

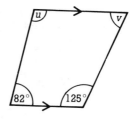

11.

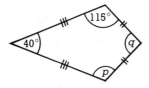

15.

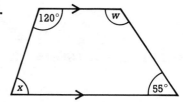

12.

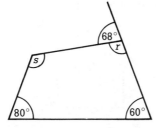

16.

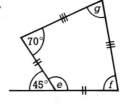

POLYGONS

A polygon is a plane (flat) figure bounded by straight lines.

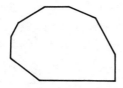

This is a 9-sided polygon.

Some polygons have names of their own:

a 3-sided polygon is a triangle

a 4-sided polygon is a quadrilateral

a 5-sided polygon is a pentagon

a 6-sided polygon is a hexagon

an 8-sided polygon is an octagon

REGULAR POLYGONS

A polygon is *regular* when *all its sides are the same length and all its angles are the same size.*

These are some regular polygons.

EXERCISE 13f State whether or not each of the following figures is a regular polygon.

1. Rhombus	**5.** Isosceles triangle
2. Square	**6.** Right-angled triangle
3. Rectangle	**7.** Equilateral triangle
4. Parallelogram	**8.** Circle

REGULAR POLYGONS AND ROTATIONAL SYMMETRY

Regular polygons have rotational symmetry.

EXERCISE 13g Write down the order of rotational symmetry of each of the following regular polygons.

1.

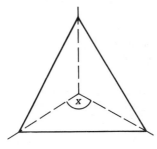

4.

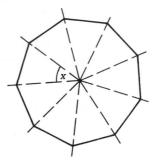

2.

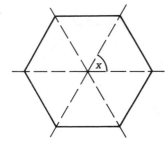

5.

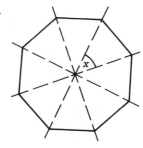

3.

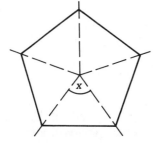

6.

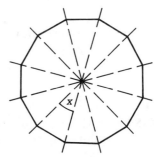

7. Find the size of the angle marked x for the polygons in questions 1 to 6.

8. Without drawing it, write down the order of rotational symmetry of a regular polygon with   a) 7 sides   b) 15 sides.

DRAWING REGULAR POLYGONS

From the last exercise we can see that

> a regular n-sided polygon has rotational symmetry of order n.

We can use this property to make accurate drawings of regular polygons.

For example, we know that a regular 8-sided polygon (octagon) has rotational symmetry of order 8.

Therefore a rotation of $\frac{1}{8}$ of a revolution leaves the polygon looking the same. ($\frac{1}{8}$ of a revolution is $\frac{1}{8}$ of 360° i.e. 45°.)

To draw a regular octagon we start at the centre O and draw the 8 "spokes" of rotational symmetry so that each one is at 45° to the next.

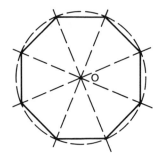

Next we draw a circle with O as its centre. Then the points where the circle cuts the "spokes" are joined with straight lines. This gives the required octagon.

EXERCISE 13h Make an accurate drawing of each of the following polygons. Remember to use a *sharp* pencil. You will also need your protractor and a ruler.

1. A regular hexagon   **4.** A regular octagon

2. An equilateral triangle   **5.** A regular pentagon

3. A square   **6.** A regular 10-sided polygon

THE EXTERIOR ANGLES OF A POLYGON

If we produce (extend) one side of a polygon, an angle is formed outside the polygon. It is called an exterior angle.

The angle marked x is an exterior angle.

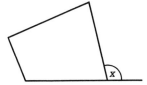

To form all the exterior angles of a polygon we produce all the sides *in order*.

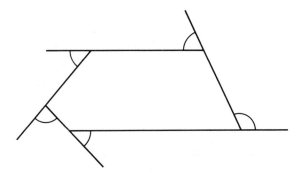

The diagram shows the five exterior angles of a pentagon.
The number of exterior angles is the same as the number of sides.

EXERCISE 13i 1. Sketch the triangle ABC and find
  a) the size of each marked angle
  b) the sum of the exterior angles.

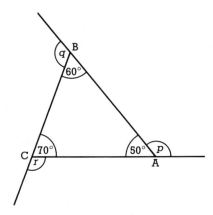

2. Sketch the quadrilateral ABCD and find
   a) the size of each marked angle
   b) the sum of the exterior angles.

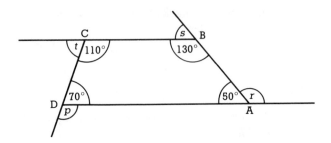

3. Sketch the pentagon given below and find
   a) the size of each marked angle
   b) the sum of the exterior angles.

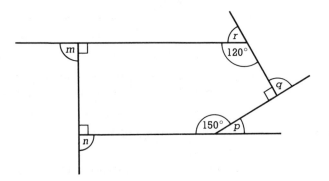

4. Find the sum of the exterior angles of △ABC.

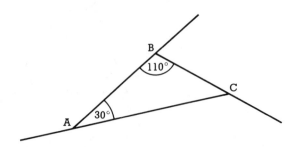

THE SUM OF THE EXTERIOR ANGLES OF A POLYGON ━━━━━

In the last exercise, the sum of the exterior angles came to 360° in each case. This is true of any polygon, whatever its shape or size.

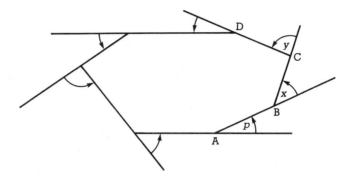

Imagine walking round this polygon. Start at A and walk along AB. When you get to B you have to turn through angle x to walk along BC. When you get to C you have to turn through angle y to walk along CD, ... and so on until you return to A. If you then turn through angle p you are facing in the direction AB again.

You have now turned through every exterior angle and have made one complete turn, i.e.

> the sum of the exterior angles of any polygon is 360°

EXERCISE 13j

Find the size of the angle marked x.

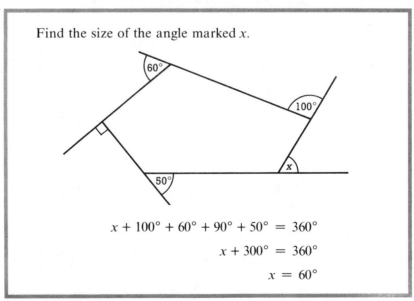

$$x + 100° + 60° + 90° + 50° = 360°$$
$$x + 300° = 360°$$
$$x = 60°$$

Find the size of the angle marked *x*.

1.
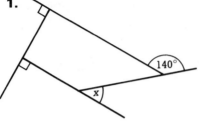

5.
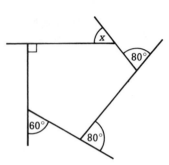

2.
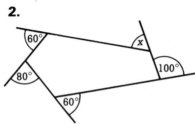

6.
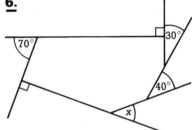

3.
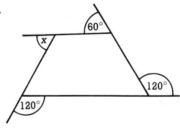

7.
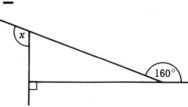

4.
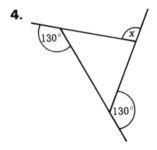

8.
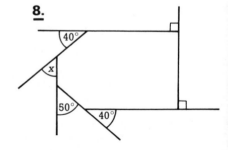

9. Sketch a *regular hexagon*, and produce each side to form an exterior angle.

    a) Write down the sum of the exterior angles.

    b) Are the sizes of these angles related in any way?

    c) Find the size of each exterior angle.

10. Repeat question 9 with a regular pentagon.

11. Repeat question 9 with a regular octagon.

12. Repeat question 9 with a regular 12-sided figure.

13. The diagram shows part of a regular 20-sided polygon.

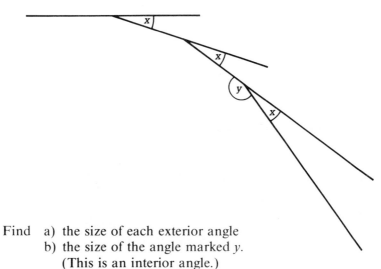

Find a) the size of each exterior angle
       b) the size of the angle marked y.
         (This is an interior angle.)

14. Use the ideas of question 13 to find the size of each interior angle in

    a) a regular hexagon

    b) a regular pentagon.

15. In a regular polygon the size of each exterior angle is $20°$. How many sides has the polygon?

16. In a regular 9-sided polygon find the size of each exterior angle.

INTERIOR ANGLES

The angles enclosed by the sides of a polygon are the interior angles.

For example

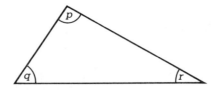

p, *q* and *r* are the interior angles of the triangle

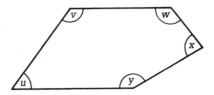

u, *v*, *w*, *x* and *y* are the interior angles of the polygon.

THE SUM OF INTERIOR ANGLES

We know that the sum of the exterior angles of any polygon is 360°.

We can use this fact to find the sum of the interior angles of any polygon.

Unless we are told that a polygon is regular we must assume that it is not. Consider a pentagon.

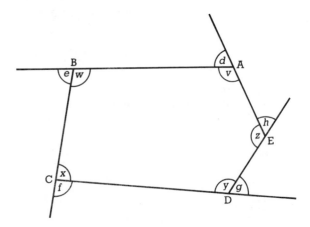

At each vertex the sum of the interior and exterior angles is $180°$, e.g. at A, $v + d = 180°$

There are five vertices, so the sum of *all* the exterior angles and *all* the interior angles is $5 \times 180° = 900°$

i.e. (sum of exterior angles) + (sum of interior angles) = $900°$

But the sum of the exterior angles is $360°$,

therefore $360° + $ (sum of interior angles) $= 900°$

Taking $360°$ from both sides gives

$$\text{sum of interior angles} = 900° - 360°$$

$$= 540°$$

EXERCISE 13k

Find the sum of the interior angles of a 9-sided polygon.

There are nine vertices so the sum of all the exterior angles and all the interior angles is $9 \times 180° = 1620°$

Sum of exterior angles is $360°$

$\therefore$ sum of interior angles is $1620° - 360°$

$$= 1260°$$

In each question from 1 to 6 find the sum of the interior angles for the named figure.

1. A pentagon   **4.** A quadrilateral

2. A 10-sided polygon   **5.** A 12-sided polygon

3. A hexagon   **6.** An octagon

For each of the following polygons find

a) the sum of all the interior angles
b) the size of the angle marked x.

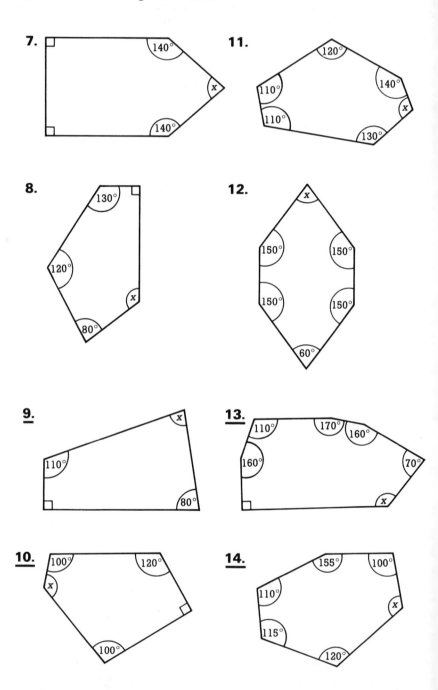

7. 140° x 140°

11. 120° 110° 140° 110° x 130°

8. 130° 120° x 80°

12. x 150° 150° 150° 150° 60°

9. x 110° 80°

13. 110° 170° 160° 160° 70° x

10. 100° 120° x 100°

14. 155° 100° 110° x 115° 120°

For a regular octagon find the size of
a) each exterior angle   b) each interior angle.

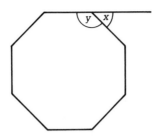

a) (The polygon is regular so the exterior angles are all
the same size: there are 8 of them and they add up to
360°.)

$$8x = 360°$$

$$x = 45°$$

Each exterior angle is 45°.

b) (The polygon is regular so the interior angles are all
the same size: at each vertex $x + y = 180°$.)

$$45° + y = 180°$$

Take 45° from each side $y = 135°$

Each interior angle is 135°.

For each of the following polygons find the size of
a) each exterior angle   b) each interior angle.

15. A regular pentagon   **19.** A regular 10-sided polygon

16. A regular hexagon   **20.** A regular 12-sided polygon

17. A regular octagon   **21.** A regular 20-sided polygon

18. A regular quadrilateral   **22.** A regular 3-sided polygon

23. In question 15 we found the size of an interior angle of a regular pentagon. Draw a rough sketch of the pentagon and mark in the size of each interior angle. Now draw, as accurately as you can, a regular pentagon with sides each 5 cm long.

24. Repeat question 23 for a regular hexagon.

TESSELLATIONS

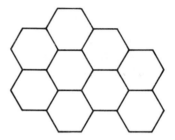

From the diagram we can see that regular hexagons fit together, without gaps, to form a flat surface.

When shapes do this we say that they *tessellate*.

Regular hexagons tessellate because each interior angle of a regular hexagon is 120°, so three vertices fit together to make 360°.

EXERCISE 13I 1.

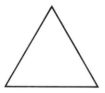

Trace this equilateral triangle and use it to cut out a template.

Using your template to draw round, show that you can cover an area of paper with equilateral triangles without any gaps, i.e. show that equilateral triangles tessellate.

2. Use squared paper to show that squares tessellate.

3. Regular hexagons, squares and equilateral triangles can be combined to make interesting patterns. Some examples are given below:

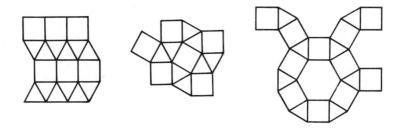

Copy these patterns and extend them. (If you make templates to help you, make each shape of side 2 cm.)

4. Make some patterns of your own using the shapes in question 3.

5. 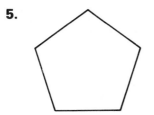 Trace this regular pentagon and use it to cut out a template.

a) Will pentagons tessellate?

b) Use your template to copy and continue this pattern until you have a complete circle of pentagons. What shape is left in the middle?

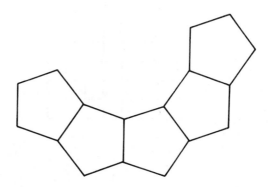

Not all regular polygons tessellate.

6.   This is a pattern using regular octagons. They do not tessellate.

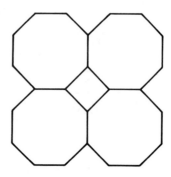

a) Explain why they do not tessellate.
b) What shape is left between the four octagons?
c) Continue the pattern. (Trace one of the shapes above, cut it out and use it as a template.)

OTHER SHAPES THAT TESSELLATE

We can build up compound shapes using squares and equilateral triangles.

This shape, for example, is made from three squares and tessellates as shown below.

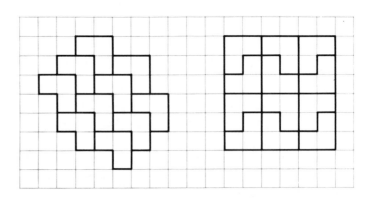

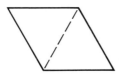 This shape is made from two equilateral triangles.

The diagram below shows a tessellation of the rhombus.

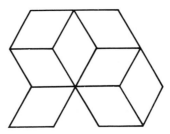

Not all compound shapes tessellate: this one, for example, does not.

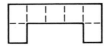

EXERCISE 13m Use squared paper to make some patterns of your own from tessellations of the following shapes.

1.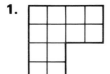

2.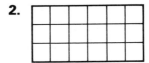

3.

4.

5.

6. Make up your own shape from squares. Make a pattern from tessellations of your own shape but remember that not all shapes will work.

Trace the following shapes on to stiff paper. Cut them out and use them as templates to make tessellations.

7.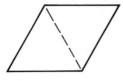

9.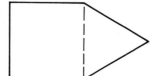

8.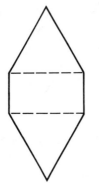

10.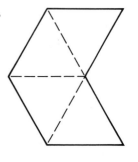

14 MORE EQUATIONS AND FORMULAE

NEW EQUATIONS

The equations that we have dealt with so far have been of the form

$$2x - 3 = 9 \quad \text{or} \quad 4y + 1 = 10$$

We have been able to solve them without guesswork by first taking a number from each side or adding a number to each side.

A simple version of the new type of equation, such as $7 - x = 4$, can be solved easily by guesswork, but if we want a more organised method we will have to do something different from before.

We can add letters to each side;

$$7 - x = 4$$

Add x to each side $\qquad (-x + x = 0, \text{ so } x \text{ disappears}$

$$7 \quad = 4 + x \qquad \text{from the left-hand side.})$$

Now we have a familiar equation and can solve it in the usual way by taking 4 from each side.

$$3 = x$$

> If the letter term has a minus sign, start by adding letters.

EXERCISE 14a

Solve $\quad 8 - y = 3$

$$8 - y = 3$$

Add y to each side $\qquad 8 = 3 + y$

Take 3 from each side $\qquad 5 = y$

i.e. $\qquad y = 5$

−y GOES FROM THE LEFT-HAND SIDE BECAUSE −y + y = 0.

Solve the following equations.

1. $7 - x = 1$	**5.** $9 - x = 5$	**9.** $7 - a = 2$
2. $9 - c = 2$	**6.** $12 - d = 7$	**10.** $10 - b = 3$
3. $5 - a = 4$	**7.** $40 - z = 25$	**11.** $24 - c = 20$
4. $12 - b = 6$	**8.** $17 - b = 9$	**12.** $6 - d = 6$

THREE STEPS

The equations in Exercise 14a were simple enough for us to be able to spot the value of the letter but the organised method becomes more useful with equations of the type $10 - 3x = 1$.

EXERCISE 14b

Solve the equation $10 - 3x = 1$

$$10 - 3x = 1$$

Add $3x$ to each side $10 = 1 + 3x$ (On the left-hand side,

$$-3x + 3x = 0)$$

Take 1 from each side $9 = 3x$

Divide each side by 3 $3 = x$

i.e. $x = 3$

Solve the following equations.

1. $9 - 2x = 1$	**5.** $13 - 3x = 10$	**9.** $21 - 2x = 13$
2. $5 - 3z = 2$	**6.** $19 - 4c = 3$	**10.** $10 - 3a = 1$
3. $12 - 5x = 2$	**7.** $11 - 2a = 1$	**11.** $17 - 4c = 5$
4. $10 - 3z = 4$	**8.** $16 - 7x = 2$	**12.** $36 - 7z = 8$

MIXED EQUATIONS

It is important to be able to recognise which sort of equation we are dealing with.

EXERCISE 14c For each of the following equations,

write A if it can be solved easily by looking,

write B if you need to add letters first,

write C if you can go straight to adding or subtracting a number.

Do not solve any of the equations yet.

1. $x + 2 = 6$	**5.** $11 - 2z = 7$	**9.** $5z - 4 = 6$
2. $2x + 5 = 13$	**6.** $9 + c = 15$	**10.** $z + 4 = 9$
3. $9 - x = 3$	**7.** $9 - c = 3$	**11.** $4 = 9 - z$
4. $3a - 4 = 17$	**8.** $13 - 3x = 4$	**12.** $4 = 9 - 5z$

Now go back and solve each equation.

Solve the following equations.

13. $4x + 3 = 19$	**17.** $s - 13 = 15$	**21.** $4z - 7 = 25$
14. $4x - 1 = 19$	**18.** $13 - s = 10$	**22.** $21 - 4z = 5$
15. $19 - 4x = 3$	**19.** $6 = s + 2$	**23.** $5 + 4z = 25$
16. $s + 13 = 15$	**20.** $13 - 2s = 3$	**24.** $z + 2 = 25$

FORMULAE

If we are using a formula and we wish to find the value of a letter that is on the right-hand side, we sometimes find that we have an equation to solve.

EXERCISE 14d

If $a = b - 2c$, find c when $a = 11$ and $b = 23$.

$$a = b - 2c$$
$$a = 11, \quad b = 23$$
$$11 = 23 - 2c$$

Add $2c$ to each side $2c + 11 = 23$

Take 11 from each side $2c = 12$

Divide each side by 2 $c = 6$

1. If $z = x - y$, find y when $z = 2$ and $x = 10$.

2. If $p = 2q - r$, find r when $p = 12$ and $q = 8$.

3. If $x = y - 3z$, find z when $x = 3$ and $y = 9$.

4. If $p = 2q - 3r$, find r when $p = 2$ and $q = 4$.

5. Given that $a = 2b - c$,
   a) find a when $b = 6$, $c = 2$.
   b) find b when $a = 8$, $c = 4$.
   c) find c when $a = 9$, $b = 6$.

6. Given that $P = 3Q - 4R$,
   a) find P when $Q = 4$, $R = 1$.
   b) find Q when $P = 13$, $R = 2$.
   c) find R when $P = 20$, $Q = 12$.

7. The basic cost of a holiday is £B. A deduction is made for the number of weeks it is paid in advance. The actual cost is £C and £2 is taken off for each week by which it is paid early.
   The formula for C is $C = B - 2x$ where x is the number of weeks.
   a) When $B = 240$ and $x = 6$, find C.
   b) When $C = 350$ and $x = 2$, find B.
   c) When $C = 340$ and $B = 360$, find x.

8. A lorry which can carry W tons is partly loaded with x cartons of Orango.
   The remaining space will take y cartons of Applefresh and the formula for y is $y = 12W - 2x$
   a) When $W = 10$ and $x = 40$, find y.
   b) When $W = 8$ and $y = 30$, find x.
   c) The lorry can carry 6 tons and there are 52 cartons of Applefresh. How many cartons of Orango can be loaded?

15 BEARINGS

COMPASS DIRECTIONS

A compass is used to find the direction of one place from another.

There are four main directions on a compass; they are north, south, east and west.
The angles separating the main directions are each 90°.
When an object is exactly in one of these main directions we say that it is *due north*, *due east* etc.

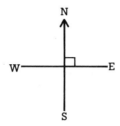

In between the main directions there are four more; they are north-east (NE), south-east (SE), south-west (SW) and north-west (NW).
Each of the eight angles in this diagram is 45°.

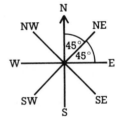

EXERCISE 15a   **1.**   This map shows the positions of three towns.

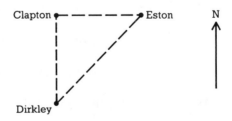

a) What is the direction of Eston from Dirkley?

b) What is the direction of Dirkley from Eston?

c) What is the direction of Clapton from Eston?

This map shows some of the landmarks in a village.

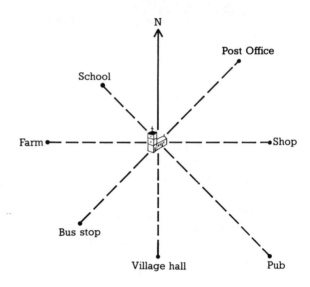

2. Which place is south-west of the church?

3. What is the direction of the school from the church?

4. Is the shop due west or due east of the farm?

5. What is the direction of the Post Office from the church?

6. In which direction is the church from the village hall?

7. Which place is south-east of the school?

8. What is the direction of the pub from the church?

9. Which place is due west of the church?

10. What is the direction of the shop from the pub?

11. In which direction is the pub from the village hall?

12. What is the direction of the school from the farm?

13. What is the direction of the farm from the school?

There are seven trees in part of the garden of Mulberry Manor. Use this plan to answer the following questions.

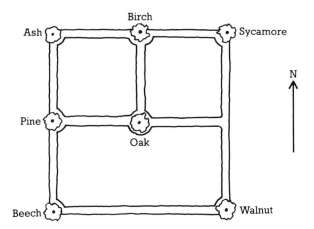

In questions 14 to 18 you are standing beside the oak tree.

14. Which tree is due west?

15. If you face SE, which tree do you see?

16. If you start facing the walnut tree and turn clockwise (↻) to face the beech tree, through what angle have you turned?

17. Which tree do you see to the NW?

18. You are facing the birch tree and turn to face the pine tree. There are two ways of doing this; in each case give the angle you have turned through and the direction of turning.

19. You can see the oak tree if you look NW and the sycamore if you look due north. Which tree are you standing beside?

20. If you stand by the beech tree and face NE, which two trees can you see?

21. You can see the oak tree if you look SE and the pine tree if you look due south. Which tree are you standing beside?

22. You can see two trees if you look SW; one of them is the beech tree. Which tree are you standing beside?

THREE-FIGURE BEARINGS

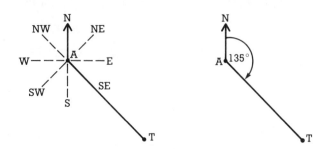

If you are standing at point A, looking at a tower, T, then you can say that from A the bearing of the tower is south-east.

Another way to give the direction of the tower from A is to use a *three-figure bearing*.

For this method we first look north and then turn clockwise (↻) until we face the tower. We have turned through 135°.

The *three-figure bearing* of the tower is 135°.

> A three-figure bearing is a clockwise angle
> measured from due north.

If the angle is less than 100° we put a zero in front to make it into a three-figure angle, e.g. a bearing of 20° is written as 020°.

EXERCISE 15b

Draw a rough sketch to show that the bearing of a barn, B, from a farmhouse, F, is 030°. Mark the angle in your sketch.

From a ship, S, the bearing of a lighthouse, L, is 200°.
Draw a rough sketch and mark the angle on it.

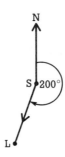

Draw a rough sketch to illustrate each of the following bearings.
Mark the angle in your sketch.

1.   From a ship, P, the bearing of a yacht, Q, is 045°

2.   From a control tower, F, the bearing of an aeroplane, A, is 090°

3.   From a point, A, the bearing of a radio mast, M, is 120°

4.   From a town, T, the bearing of another town, S, is 180°

5.   From a point, H, the bearing of a church, C, is 210°

6.   From a ship, R, the bearing of a port, P, is 300°

7.   From an aircraft, A, the bearing of an airport, L, is 320°

8.   From a town, D, the bearing of another town, E, is 260°

9.   From a helicopter, G, the bearing of a landing pad, P, is 060°

10.   From a point, L, the bearing of a tree, T, is 270°

11.   The bearing of a ship, A, from the pier, P, is 225°

12.   The bearing of a radio mast, S, from a point, P, is 140°

13.   The bearing of a yacht, Y, from a tanker, T, is 075°

EXERCISE 15c In each question write down the three-figure bearing of B from A.

1.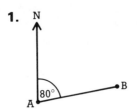

3.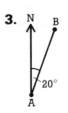

5.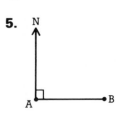

2.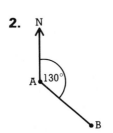

4.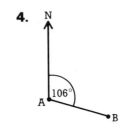

6.

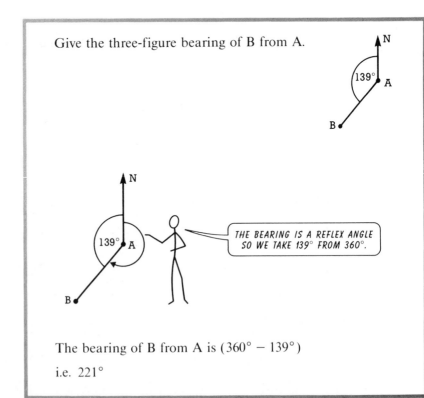

Give the three-figure bearing of B from A.

THE BEARING IS A REFLEX ANGLE SO WE TAKE 139° FROM 360°.

The bearing of B from A is $(360° - 139°)$

i.e. $221°$

In questions 7 to 12, write down the three-figure bearing of B from A.

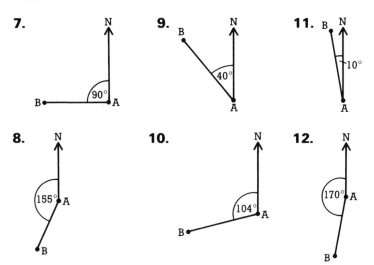

For each question from 13 to 18, draw a sketch showing the two given towns, with the angle and the distance from one to the other. The first one is done for you.

13. The bearing of Broughing from Lowton is 050° and the distance is 5 km.

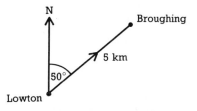

14. The bearing of Grove from Lester is 150° and the distance is 51 km.

15. From Easton, Grately is on a bearing of 020° and is 25 km away.

16. Stabing is 14 km from Reech on a bearing of 235°.

17. Welton is on a bearing of 095° from Eskly and they are 10 miles apart.

18. Tingley is 14 km from Raughten on a bearing of 285°.

EXERCISE 15d To answer questions 1 to 8 you need a full size copy of this map from Copymaster 3.

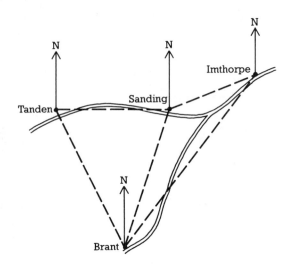

1. a) On your copy of the map mark the angle which gives the bearing of Sanding from Brant.
    b) Measure this angle with a protractor.
    c) Write down the three-figure bearing of Sanding from Brant.

2. a) Mark the angle which gives the bearing of Brant from Tanden.
    b) Measure this angle.
    c) Write down the three-figure bearing of Brant from Tanden.

3. a) Mark the angle which gives the bearing of Imthorpe from Sanding.
    b) Measure this angle.
    c) Write down the three-figure bearing of Imthorpe from Sanding.

4. a) Mark the angle which gives the bearing of Sanding from Tanden.
    b) Measure this angle.
    c) Write down the three-figure bearing of Sanding from Tanden.
    d) Is there another way to give the direction of Sanding from Tanden?

Mark the angle which gives the bearing of Brant from Sanding. Find the three-figure bearing of Brant from Sanding.

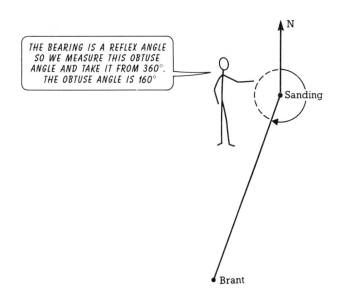

THE BEARING IS A REFLEX ANGLE
SO WE MEASURE THIS OBTUSE
ANGLE AND TAKE IT FROM 360°.
THE OBTUSE ANGLE IS 160°

From Sanding the bearing of Brant is $360° - 160° = 200°$.

Use your copy of the map again for questions 5 to 8.

5. a) Mark the angle which gives the bearing of Sanding from Imthorpe.
  b) Find the three-figure bearing of Sanding from Imthorpe.

6. a) Mark the angle which gives the bearing of Tanden from Brant.
  b) Find the three-figure bearing of Tanden from Brant.

7. a) Mark the angle which gives the bearing of Brant from Imthorpe.
  b) Find the three-figure bearing of Brant from Imthorpe.

8. a) Mark the angle which gives the bearing of Tanden from Sanding.
  b) Find the three-figure bearing of Tanden from Sanding.

EXERCISE 15e For this exercise you need a copy of the map from Copymaster 4.

Find the three-figure bearing of Morch from Flint.

First draw the north line through Flint (lay a ruler through Flint, parallel to the grid lines). Then join Flint to Morch. Mark and measure the angle which gives the bearing of Morch from Flint.

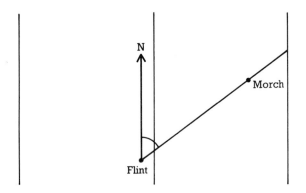

The bearing of Flint from Morch is . . . .

---

1.   Find the three-figure bearing of Lynn from Brent End.

2.   What is the three-figure bearing of Byfield from Birn?

3.   Find the three-figure bearing of Ryton from Flint.

4.   What is the three-figure bearing of Byfield from Ryton?

5.   Find the three-figure bearing of Brent End from Eyton.

Say whether each of the following statements is true or false.

6.   The bearing of Birn from Lynn is about 030°.

7.   From Morch the bearing of Eyton is about 270°.

8.   The bearing of Eyton from Flint is about 045°.

16 INEQUALITIES

NUMBER LINE

We have seen that the scale on a number line can contain negative numbers and zero as well as positive numbers and it can be extended as far as we like in each direction. So every number has a place on a number line.

COMPARING NUMBERS

To compare any two numbers on the line we say that the one on the *right* is *greater than* the one on the left.

For example,
    7 is greater than 3
    5 is greater than 0
    2 is greater than −1
    −2 is greater than −4

The symbol $>$ stands for "is greater than" so we can write the statements above in a neater form.

i.e.
$$7 > 3;$$
$$5 > 0;$$
$$2 > -1;$$
$$-2 > -4$$

A number on the *left* of another number on the line is said to be *less than* that number. We use the symbol $<$ for "is less than".

For example,
$$-5 < -3;$$
$$-2 < 0;$$
$$-1 < 3;$$
$$2 < 7$$

203

EXERCISE 16a This number line shows the scale on a thermometer, in °C. It will help in answering questions 1 to 9.

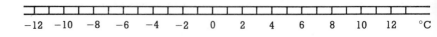

Say whether each statement is true or false,

a) $-4\,°C < 1\,°C$ b) $-2\,°C < -3\,°C$

a) $-4\,°C$ is on the left of $1\,°C$ so $-4\,°C < 1\,°C$ is true.

b) $-2\,°C$ is on the right of $-3\,°C$ so $-2\,°C < -3\,°C$ is false.

State whether each statement is true or false.

1. $3\,°C > 0\,°C$ **4.** $7\,°C > -4\,°C$ **7.** $-8\,°C > -6\,°C$

2. $-3\,°C > 0\,°C$ **5.** $1\,°C > -1\,°C$ **8.** $3\,°C < 7\,°C$

3. $4\,°C > -7\,°C$ **6.** $-1\,°C > 0\,°C$ **9.** $-4\,°C < -6\,°C$

This line will help in answering questions 10 to 23.

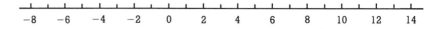

Insert $>$ or $<$ between each pair of numbers,

a) -1 4 b) -2 -6

a) -1 is on the left of 4

$$-1 < 4$$

b) -2 is on the right of -6

$$-2 > -6$$

Insert > or < between each pair of numbers.

10.	9	4	**17.**	8	−3
11.	10	3	**18.**	−5	12
12.	7	0	**19.**	−6	−4
13.	0	8	**20.**	9	−3
14.	0	−2	**21.**	−5	9
15.	−5	1	**22.**	8	11
16.	−7	−2	**23.**	8	−11

INEQUALITIES CONTAINING UNKNOWN VALUES

Listening to a weather forecast you might hear the announcer say "The temperature tonight will be above 4 °C".

This does not tell us exactly what the temperature is going to be so we can call it x °C. However, we *do* know that x °C > 4 °C,

i.e. $x > 4$

This is an *inequality* and it is true when the value of x is any number greater than 4, but not 4 itself.

We say that any number greater than 4 *satisfies* the inequality.

There is a range of values of x that satisfies the inequality $x > 4$ and we can show this range on a number line.

We can use an "open" circle at 4 to indicate that x cannot be *equal* to 4.

Similarly, if a regulation restricts the number of passengers in a chair-lift to less than 7, then if n is the number of passengers,

$n < 7$

i.e.

EXERCISE 16b

Use a number line to illustrate the range of values of x
for which   a) $x < -1$ b) $x > -3.5$

a)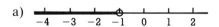

b)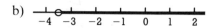

Use a number line to illustrate the range of values of x for which
each of the given inequalities is true.

1. $x > 6$	**5.** $x > 8$	**9.** $x > 4$
2. $x < 5$	**6.** $x < 3$	**10.** $x < 6$
3. $x > -4$	**7.** $x > -3$	**11.** $x < -5$
4. $x < -2$	**8.** $x < -1$	**12.** $x > -7$

13. $x > 0$	**16.** $x < 0$	**19.** $x < \frac{1}{2}$
14. $x > 2.5$	**17.** $x > 0.5$	**20.** $x < -0.5$
15. $x < 1.5$	**18.** $x > -2.5$	**21.** $x > -1.5$

22.   "The temperature tonight will be below freezing".

a) If the temperature tonight is x °C, write an inequality for x.
b) Illustrate your inequality on a number line.

23.   I have to keep more than £20 in my bank account. If I have
£x in my account at the moment,

a) write an inequality for x,
b) illustrate your inequality on a number line.

24.   To earn a bonus Tim Hall has to assemble more than 25 fan
heaters in a day. Yesterday Tim assembled x fan heaters and
got a bonus.

a) Write an inequality for x.
b) Illustrate your inequality on a number line.

CHECKING VALUES IN AN INEQUALITY ▬▬▬▬▬▬▬▬▬▬

EXERCISE 16c

> Last night the weather forecaster said that the temperature would not fall below $-5°C$. The minimum reading on my greenhouse thermometer was $-3°C$. Was the forecast correct?
>
> If $x°C$ was the temperature during last night then, from the forecast,
>
> $$x > -5$$
>
> We can illustrate this on a number line.
>
>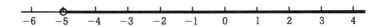
>
> Now -3 is in the range that satisfies the inequality $x > -5$
> Therefore the forecast was correct.

State whether or not the given value satisfies the given inequality.

1. $x = 3,\ x < 6$

2. $x = 5,\ x > -3$

3. $x = -4,\ x < 3$

4. $x = 0,\ x < -5$

5. $x = -2,\ x > -1$

6. $x = 7,\ x > 8$

7. $x = 8,\ x > 0$

8. $x = -3,\ x < 12$

9. $x = -2,\ x > -5$

10. $x = 0,\ x > -4$

11. Sian Thomas has arranged with her bank manager that she can overdraw her account to $-£50$. Her latest statement shows that her balance is $-£32$. Has she kept to her arrangement?

12. A skuba diver can safely go 400 centimetres below the surface of the water, i.e. to a distance of -400 cm from the surface. Is he safe when his gauge reads -350 cm?

NUMBERS THAT SATISFY INEQUALITIES

EXERCISE 16d

Write down a whole number which satisfies the inequality
$x < -2$

The number could be −5.

(It could also be −3, −7, or *any* number to the left of −2.)

In each of the following questions, write down any two whole numbers which satisfy the given inequality.

1. $x > 5$ **7.** $x > 2$

2. $x > -3$ **8.** $x > -7$

3. $x < -4$ **9.** $x < -9$

4. $x > 5.7$ **10.** $x < 3.2$

5. $x < -4.5$ **11.** $x > -2.6$

6. $x > -0.2$ **12.** $x < 0.9$

EXERCISE 16e

Give the smallest even whole number that satisfies the inequality $x > 10$

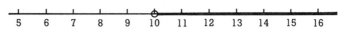

The next even number to the right of 10 on the number line is 12.

In each question from 1 to 6, give the smallest whole number that satisfies the given inequality.

1. $x > 12$ **3.** $x > 0$ **5.** $x > 20$

2. $x > -4$ **4.** $x > -18$ **6.** $x > -9$

In each question from 7 to 12, give the largest whole number that satisfies the given inequality.

7. $x < 8$ **9.** $x < -5$ **11.** $x < 18$

8. $x < 0$ **10.** $x < -10$ **12.** $x < -15$

In each question from 13 to 18, give the smallest prime number that satisfies the inequality.

13. $x > 8$ **15.** $x > 9$ **17.** $x > 20$

14. $x > 3$ **16.** $x > 17$ **18.** $x > 30$

In each question from 19 to 24, give the largest prime number that satisfies the inequality.

19. $x < 10$ **21.** $x < 20$ **23.** $x < 25$

20. $x < 8$ **22.** $x < 3$ **24.** $x < 30$

25. Give the largest whole number that is exactly divisible by 5 and which satisfies the inequality $x < 29$

26. Give the smallest whole number that is exactly divisible by 7 and which satisfies the inequality $x > 36$

27. Give the largest whole number that is exactly divisible by 2 and by 3 and which satisfies the inequality $x < 35$

28. Give the smallest whole number that is exactly divisible by 3 and by 4 and which satisfies the inequality $x > 45$

29. Give the smallest whole number that is exactly divisible by 5 and 7 and which satisfies the inequality $x > 40$

30. Give the largest whole number that is exactly divisible by 3 and 5 and which satisfies the inequality $x < 40$

31. Give the largest whole number that is exactly divisible by 2, 3 and 5 and which satisfies the inequality $x < 50$

32. Give the smallest whole number that is exactly divisible by 3, 4 and 5 and which satisfies the inequality $x > 100$

WORKING WITH INEQUALITIES

Suppose that we have one pile of 5 *Oxo* cubes and another pile of 3 *Oxo* cubes.

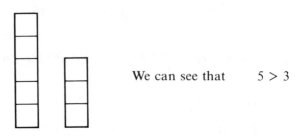

We can see that   5 > 3

Now let us add 3 cubes to each pile.

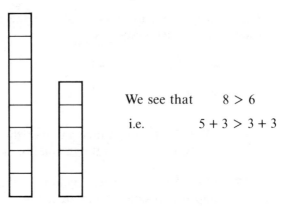

We see that   8 > 6

i.e.   5 + 3 > 3 + 3

Starting again with the original piles of cubes, we will now take 2 cubes away from each pile.

This time   3 > 1

i.e.   5 − 2 > 3 − 2

If we add 3 to each side of 5 > 3 we get 8 > 6, which is still true. If we subtract 2 from each side we get 3 > 1, which is still true.

If we add other numbers to each side, or subtract other numbers from each side, we get a true inequality each time.

An inequality remains true when the *same* number is added to, or subtracted from, both sides.

EXERCISE 16f

Given the inequality $3 > -1$
a) add 2 to each side   b) subtract 2 from each side.

a)

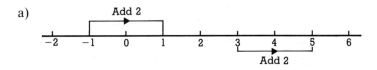

$$3 > -1$$
$$5 > 1$$

b)

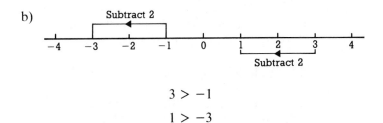

$$3 > -1$$
$$1 > -3$$

1. Subtract 3 from each side of the inequality $9 > 3$

2. Add 4 to each side of the inequality $7 < 12$

3. Subtract 6 from each side of the inequality $8 > -1$

4. Add 2 to each side of the inequality $-3 < 2$

5. Add 3 to each side of the inequality $-5 < 0$

6. Subtract 5 from each side of the inequality $8 < 12$

7. Subtract 10 from each side of the inequality $9 < 16$

8. Add 4 to each side of the inequality $5 > -1$

9. Add 6 to each side of the inequality $-7 < -3$

10. Subtract 4 from each side of the inequality $-5 < -4$

Add 4 to each side of the inequality $x - 4 > 7$. The result is a range of values of x; illustrate this on a number line.

$$x - 4 > 7$$

$$x > 11$$

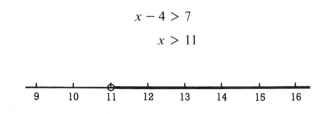

In each question from 11 to 18 the result is a range of values of x. Illustrate this on a number line.

11. Add 6 to each side of the inequality $x - 6 > 3$

12. Add 8 to each side of the inequality $x - 8 < 9$

13. Subtract 3 from each side of the inequality $x + 3 > 12$

14. Subtract 4 from each side of the inequality $x + 4 > 7$

15. Subtract 8 from each side of the inequality $x + 8 < 16$

16. Add 10 to each side of the inequality $x - 10 > -14$

17. Subtract 5 from each side of the inequality $x + 5 < 8$

18. Subtract 6 from each side of the inequality $x + 6 < -7$

INEQUALITIES INCLUDING AN EQUALITY

Suppose that a teacher says that he will organise an outing to a farm provided that at least 12 pupils wish to go. This means that the number of pupils can be exactly 12 or any number greater than 12.

If x pupils want to go, the visit can take place if

$$x = 12 \quad \text{or} \quad x > 12$$

We can combine these two conditions and write

$$x \geqslant 12$$

The symbol $\geqslant$ means "greater than or equal to".

Similarly we use $\leqslant$ when we want to write "less than or equal to".

EXERCISE 16g

a) The minimum number of days for which a holiday bungalow can be booked is 7. If x is the number of days, write a statement for x, using $\geqslant$ or $\leqslant$.

b) A theatre is licensed to seat 600 people. If x is the number of tickets sold for a performance, write a statement for x, using $\geqslant$ or $\leqslant$.

a) The number of days can be 7 or more than 7.

$$x \geqslant 7$$

b) The number of tickets can be any number below 600 or 600 itself.

$$x \leqslant 600$$

In each question use $\geqslant$ or $\leqslant$ to write a statement for x.

1. The Bigtime Basketball Club will accept applications for membership only from players who are at least 6 feet tall. Take x feet as the height of a successful applicant.

2. A notice at the Pleasure Cruise ticket office states that the maximum number of passengers is 50. Take x as the number of passengers.

3. At the local petrol station the pumps will not dispense less than 5 litres of petrol. I buy x litres.

4. Correctly mixed antifreeze protects a car engine at temperatures down to $-5°C$. My engine is protected when the temperature is $x°C$.

5. A maximum of six standing passengers are permitted on a bus. The conductor allows x people to stand.

DOUBLE INEQUALITIES

Suppose that, in order to run a school bus, the number of passengers must be at least 15 and not more than 32.

Taking x as the number of passengers,
the number of passengers can be 15 or more, so $x \geqslant 15$
$$(\text{or} \quad 15 \leqslant x)$$
the number of passengers can be 32 or less, so $x \leqslant 32$

Both of these conditions have to be satisfied so we combine them by writing

$$15 \leqslant x \leqslant 32$$

This means that x can have any value from 15 up to 32 inclusive.

We can represent this on a number line as follows

The solid circles at 15 and 32 show that x *can* take these values.

Note that when we combine two inequalities in one statement, the quantities must be in order of size with x in the middle.

EXERCISE 16h

The number of matches in a box varies. Taking this number as x we are told that $30 < x \leqslant 36$.

a) Write two separate facts about x.
b) Describe these two facts in words.
c) Illustrate on a number line the possible number of matches in a box.

a) If $30 < x \leqslant 36$

   then $30 < x$ and $x \leqslant 36$

b) There are more than 30 matches in a box.

   There are not more than 36 matches in a box.

c)

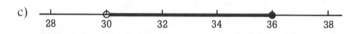

In each question from 1 to 4 write two separate facts about x and illustrate them on a number line.

1. The number of books lost by a school library in a term is x. The librarian says that $3 \leqslant x < 20$

2. A taxi-driver covers x miles a day. In one week the taxi-driver worked out that $80 \leqslant x \leqslant 305$

3. Jenny collects pine cones but she wants them each to weigh more than 100 g and does not want any that weigh more than 250 g. A suitable pine cone weighs x grams.

4. The price of a daffodil bulb is x pence. The price was checked in a number of different shops. The cheapest bulb was 7 p and the most expensive was 15 p.

A shopkeeper is ordering N tins of biscuits. He does not have room for more than 16 tins and he must order more than 6 tins. Write a statement for N and illustrate it on a number line.

He must order more than 6 tins, $N > 6$ i.e. $6 < N$

The greatest number ordered is 16, $N \leqslant 16$

Therefore $6 < N \leqslant 16$

---

5. N is any number bigger than 7 and less than 19. Write a single statement for N and illustrate it on a number line.

6. A number X is at least 5 and not more than 13. Write a single statement for X and illustrate it on a number line.

7. Rick asks Stephen to "think of any number from 3 to 8 inclusive". If Stephen thinks of the number N, write a single statement for N and illustrate it on a number line.

8. A survey is being conducted on the pocket money received by children in the age group "over 8 and up to and including 12". If x years is the age of a suitable child, write a single statement for x and illustrate it on a number line.

9. Janice does at least 30 minutes homework a night and sometimes does as much as 80 minutes. If Janice does x minutes homework tonight, write a single statement for x and illustrate it on a number line.

10. The pupils in a class were weighed. The lightest pupil weighed 26 kg and no-one weighed as much as 40 kg. If x kg is the weight of one of the pupils, write a single statement for x and illustrate it on a number line.

MIXED EXERCISES

EXERCISE 16i **1.** Copy each of the following pairs of temperatures, inserting > or < between them.

a) $-2°$ $\quad -9°$ b) $5°$ $\quad -6°$ c) $4°$ $\quad -1°$

2. Decide whether or not the given value satisfies the given inequality

a) $x = -3$, $x > -4$
b) $x = 7$, $x \leqslant 7$

3. Give two whole numbers that satisfy the inequality $x < -4.5$

4. Give the smallest whole number that satisfies the inequality

a) $x > 7$
b) $x > -5$

5. Give the largest whole number that satisfies the inequality

a) $x < 12$
b) $x < -5$

6. The minimum weight of the chocolates in a packet is 100 g. Taking x grams as the weight of the chocolates, write an inequality for x.

7. If N is a number and $2 \leqslant N \leqslant 8$, illustrate the range of values of N on a number line.

8. The youngest member of a Youth Club is aged 12 and no-one over 16 is allowed to be a member. If x is the age of a member, write a single statement showing the possible values of x.

EXERCISE 16j **1.** Use a number line to illustrate the range of values of x for which each of the following inequalities is true.
a) $x < -4$
b) $x > -7$

2. State whether each of the following statements is true or false.
a) $-5° > -1°$ b) $2° > -4°$ c) $-9° > -3°$

3. Write down two whole numbers that satisfy the inequality
$$x > 3.5$$

4. Add 4 to each side of the following inequalities.
a) $7 > -3$ b) $-11 < -1$ c) $x - 4 > 3$

5. Write a statement about the possible values of N if
a) N is less than 5
b) N is at least 2
c) N cannot be more than 10

6. The number, N, of persons in a lift must not exceed 8. Write an inequality for N.

7. Illustrate on a number line the range of values of x that is given by
$$-3 \leqslant x \leqslant 7$$

8. Each of the following diagrams shows the range of possible values of a number *N*. Write each range in inequality form.

a)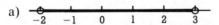

b)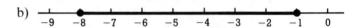

c)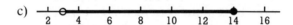

17 GROUPING AND DISPLAYING DATA

FREQUENCY TABLES AND BAR CHARTS

This information about the shoe sizes of 40 people has been collected.

2	5	$3\frac{1}{2}$	4	$4\frac{1}{2}$	$2\frac{1}{2}$	3	6	$3\frac{1}{2}$	4
5	$2\frac{1}{2}$	4	3	$3\frac{1}{2}$	3	$4\frac{1}{2}$	$5\frac{1}{2}$	4	$4\frac{1}{2}$
$5\frac{1}{2}$	6	4	2	3	5	$3\frac{1}{2}$	4	$2\frac{1}{2}$	3
3	$4\frac{1}{2}$	2	4	4	$3\frac{1}{2}$	5	3	$5\frac{1}{2}$	3

When the numbers are written down in the order in which they arise, they are called *raw data*.

This information needs sorting before it can tell us anything about the distribution of shoe sizes.

First we can see that the smallest size is 2 and the largest size is 6. The difference between the smallest and largest value in a list of data is called the *range*.

The range of shoe sizes is $6 - 2 = 4$

Next we can find out how many there are of each size and make a frequency table.

Shoe size	2	$2\frac{1}{2}$	3	$3\frac{1}{2}$	4	$4\frac{1}{2}$	5	$5\frac{1}{2}$	6	
Tally	III	III	JHT III	JHT	JHT III	IIII	IIII	III	II	Total
Frequency (number of people)	3	3	8	5	8	4	4	3	2	40

There are 40 shoe sizes listed, so the frequencies should add up to 40.

We can illustrate this information in a bar chart.
(The bars can have gaps between them as shown on the next page, or they can touch.)

219

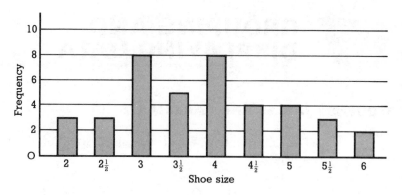

EXERCISE 17a 1. Use the bar chart above to answer these questions.

a) Which shoe size is the most common?

b) Which shoe size is the least common?

2. This bar chart shows the different pets owned by pupils in a class.

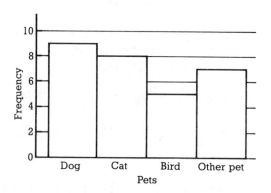

a) How many dogs are owned by pupils in the class?

b) How many birds are owned by pupils in the class?

c) Copy and complete the following frequency table.

Type of pet	Dog	Cat	Bird	Other pet
Frequency		8		

d) How many pets are there altogether?

e) Name some animals which would come under the heading "Other pet".

f) Have any of the pupils got 2 dogs?

3. The passengers getting on to a bus during its journey were placed in one of four categories. The information is given below.

M stands for man, W for woman, B for boy and G for girl.

M	W	W	W	B	G	W	M
G	G	G	M	B	M	G	M
B	G	B	B	M	M	G	B
W	W	W	W	M	M	W	M

a) Make a table similar to the table used in question 2.
b) Draw a bar chart illustrating this information.
c) How many males were there on the bus and how many females?
d) How many more girls than boys were there on the bus?

4. The pupils in a class counted the number of rooms, apart from bathrooms and kitchens, in which they and their families lived. The information is given below.

3	5	7	3	7	5	7	5	2	4
4	4	6	6	7	6	6	5	1	5
4	2	5	6	1	5	7	6	3	3

a) Make a frequency table.
b) Draw a bar chart illustrating this information.
c) What is the most common number of rooms?
d) How many rooms altogether do the pupils in this class have amongst them?

GROUPING INFORMATION

On page 219, we took each shoe size as a separate category when we made the frequency table. Because there are not very many items in some categories, the resulting bar chart looks a bit ragged. We might get a clearer picture of the distribution if we group the information so that we include each half size with the next size up. This gives the following frequency table and bar chart.

Shoe size	$1\frac{1}{2}$-2	$2\frac{1}{2}$-3	$3\frac{1}{2}$-4	$4\frac{1}{2}$-5	$5\frac{1}{2}$-6	Total
Frequency (number of people)	3	11	13	8	5	40

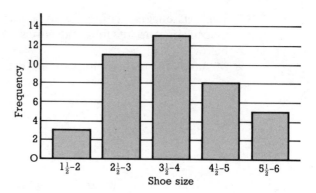

EXERCISE 17b 1. Use the bar chart above to answer these questions.

   a) Which group of shoe sizes is the most common?

   b) Can you tell from the bar chart how many people have size 5 shoes?

2. The marks gained by pupils in an examination are given below. They have been extracted from a database and are given in numerical order.

30	39	47	52	56	59	63	69	79	86
30	40	47	52	56	59	63	70	79	86
31	42	48	53	57	60	64	72	80	87
31	44	48	53	57	60	65	74	81	87
38	45	49	55	58	61	65	75	85	88
39	46	51	56	59	62	68	79	86	89
39	46	51	56	59	62	68	79	86	89

   a) Make a frequency table, using the groups 30 to 39, 40 to 49, 50 to 59, 60 to 69, 70 to 79 and 80 to 89.

   b) Draw a bar chart to illustrate this information. For the heights of the bars use 1 cm to represent 1 pupil.

3. The number of words in each of the sentences on the first page of a book were recorded. The information is given below.

9	26	11	15	21	19	29	19
15	10	6	17	12	13	25	23
11	4	13	25	21	17	16	13

   a) Form a table using the groups 1 to 5, 6 to 10, 11 to 15, 16 to 20, 21 to 25 and 26 to 29.

   b) Draw a bar chart to illustrate this information.

CONTINUOUS DATA

If we are asked to count the number of people at a bus stop the answer will be a whole number (we cannot have 3.6 people!).

On the other hand, if we find the heights of people, there is no reason why any one person's height should be a whole number of centimetres. Your own height is likely to be somewhere between 120 cm and 200 cm and could be marked anywhere along this section of a tape measure.

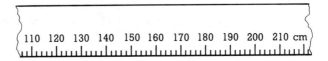

Because height can be anywhere on a continuous scale, it is not possible to have a gap in the scale and say that no person's height can be in that gap.

A collection of heights is an example of continuous data.

EXERCISE 17c State whether each of the following quantities could be

    a) a whole number only

    b) marked anywhere on a continuous scale.

    1. The number of pupils in your class.

    2. The time it took you to get to school today.

    3. The number of peas in a pod.

    4. The length of your classroom.

    5. Your weight.

    6. The volume of liquid in a bottle.

GROUPING CONTINUOUS DATA

This is a list of the heights (each given to the nearest centimetre) of 55 children. The list has been extracted from a database which has sorted the heights into numerical order.

131	134	136	137	139	141	142	144	145	147	149
132	134	136	137	139	141	142	144	145	148	150
132	134	136	138	140	142	143	144	146	148	150
133	135	136	138	140	142	143	144	147	149	152
133	135	137	139	140	142	144	145	147	149	153

The height of the shortest child is about 131 cm and the height of the tallest child is about 153 cm.

This information needs to be grouped to make more sense of it, so we will start the first group at 130 cm, the second group at 135 cm, the third group at 140 cm, and so on. This will give us five groups which we can write as

130 cm —, 135 cm —, 140 cm —, 145 cm —, 150 cm —.

Notice that *each group is the same width* so the last group includes all heights less than 155 cm.

Any height that is *less* than 135 cm belongs to the first group, but a height of 135 cm belongs to the second group.

Looking down the list of heights we can see that there are 8 children whose heights are in the first group, 14 children whose heights are in the second group, and so on. We can write this information in a frequency table.

Height	Frequency
130 cm —	8
135 cm —	14
140 cm —	17
145 cm —	12
150 cm —	4
Total	55

EXERCISE 17d 1. Use the frequency table above to answer the following questions.

a) How many children had a height less than 135 cm?

b) How many children had a height of at least 150 cm?

c) In which group do the heights of most children lie?

d) Two children were away when the survey was made. Their heights are 152 cm and 140.1 cm. Make a new frequency table to include these heights.

2. Emma kept a record of the time she had to wait for the bus to school each morning for four weeks. The results are shown in this frequency table.

Time (in minutes)	Tally	Frequency
0 —	JHT II	7
5 —	JHT IIII	9
10 —	III	3
15 —	I	1

a) On how many mornings did Emma have to wait for 15 minutes or longer?

b) How often did Emma wait less than 5 minutes?

c) On how many mornings did Emma record the length of her wait?

d) Did Emma ever have to wait for 20 minutes?

3. This is a list of the weights, in kilograms, of 100 adults. The list is in numerical order.

```
47  50  52  54  60  63  63  64  66  66  68  69  70  70  72  78  79  80  90  104
48  51  53  55  60  63  63  64  66  67  68  69  70  71  73  78  80  82  92  110
49  51  53  58  61  63  63  65  66  67  68  70  70  71  73  78  80  80  83  94  112
49  51  53  58  62  63  64  65  66  68  69  70  70  72  74  79  80  85  95  115
49  52  54  59  62  63  64  65  66  68  69  70  70  72  75  79  80  88  100  118
```

a) What is the smallest weight?

b) How many people have a weight of less than 50 kg?

c) Copy and complete this frequency table.

Weight	Frequency
40 kg —	
60 kg —	
80 kg —	
100 kg —	
Total	

d) How many people have a weight of 100 kg or more?

e) How many people have a weight of less than 80 kg?

BAR CHARTS FOR CONTINUOUS DATA ────────────────

We can use the frequency table on page 224 to draw a bar chart.

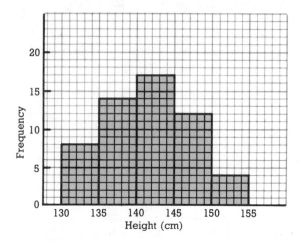

Notice that the horizontal axis gives the heights on a continuous scale, like part of a tape measure, so there are *no gaps between the bars*.

> A bar chart illustrating continuous data must not have any gaps between the bars.

EXERCISE 17e 1. Here is a frequency table showing the times, in minutes, taken by the pupils in a class on their journeys from home to school on a particular morning.

Time (in minutes)	Frequency
0 —	2
10 —	9
20 —	5
30 —	4
40 —	2
50 —	1

Copy and complete the bar chart on page 227, using the table.

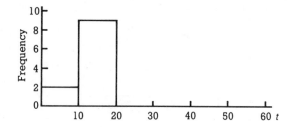

2. At the health centre, some babies were weighed one afternoon. Their weights, in kilograms, were recorded by the nurse, as tally marks in this frequency table.

Weight (in kg)	4 —	8 —	12 —
Tally	JHT II	JHT JHT I	JHT I
Frequency			

The next two babies were weighed at just under 12 kg and just over 12 kg. Add these weights to the frequency table and then complete the table.
Draw a bar chart to illustrate this information.

3. Draw a bar chart to illustrate the data given in question 2 of Exercise 17d.

4. Draw a bar chart to illustrate the data given in question 3 of Exercise 17d.

5. This is a list of the weights, in kilograms, of 30 fourteen-year-old boys.

| 50 | 55 | 57 | 60 | 61 | 64 | 65 | 65 | 65 | 67 | 67 | 68 | 68 | 69 | 70 |
| 52 | 56 | 57 | 60 | 62 | 64 | 65 | 65 | 66 | 67 | 67 | 68 | 68 | 69 | 75 |

You are asked to draw a bar chart to illustrate this data.

a) Decide on the groups that you will use and make a frequency table.

b) Draw the bar chart.

PIE CHARTS

We can use other types of diagram to illustrate the information we collect. One of these is a pie chart where the size of the slice is proportional to the frequency.

EXERCISE 17f

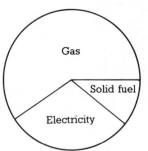

This pie chart shows the method of cooking in 60 houses in a street.

a) Which method is used least?
b) Which method is used most?
c) How does the number of houses using gas compare with the number using electricity?

a) Solid fuel is used least.

b) Gas is used most.

c) Gas is used in about twice as many houses as is electricity.

1.

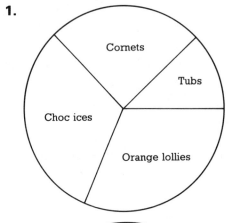

This pie chart shows the relative sales of different sorts of ice-cream.

a) Which is the least popular ice-cream?
b) The sales of one ice-cream form a quarter of the total sales. Which ice-cream is it?
c) Two ice-creams sell in equal quantities. Which two are they?

2.

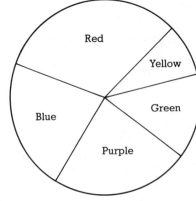

This pie chart shows the favourite colours of a group of people.

a) Which colour was the most popular?
b) Which colour was the least popular?
c) Which two colours were chosen by approximately the same number of people?

3.

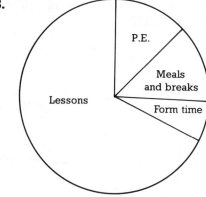

This pie chart shows the amounts of time spent on different activities in school.

a) Which activity has least time spent on it?

b) On which two activities are equal amounts of time spent?

The proceeds from a jumble sale were £520.

This pie chart shows how this money was allocated.

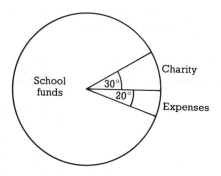

What amount was given to charity?

The angle at the centre of the slice marked "Charity" is 30°.

So the amount given to charity is $\frac{30}{360}$ of the proceeds

i.e. $\frac{30}{360} \times £520$

$= 0.0833 \ldots \times £520$

$= £43.33$ to the nearest penny

4. This pie chart shows the costs involved in making a television set. The total cost is £180.

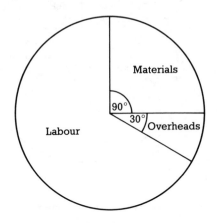

    a) What fraction of the total cost is the cost of materials?
    b) What fraction of the total cost is the cost of overheads?
    c) What is the cost of materials?
    d) What is the cost of overheads?
    e) What are the labour costs?

5. When 360 pupils were asked what they did on Saturday evening they gave the information shown in this pie chart.

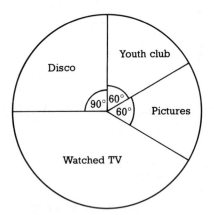

    a) What fraction of the total number of pupils went to a disco?
    b) What fraction of the total number of pupils went to a Youth Club?
    c) How many went to a disco?
    d) How many went to a Youth Club?
    e) How many watched T.V.?

6.

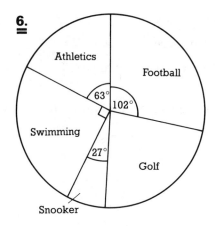

This pie chart shows the favourite sport of a group of 120 teenagers.

a) What fraction chose swimming?

b) How many chose athletics?

c) How many more chose football than snooker?

d) How many chose golf?

7.

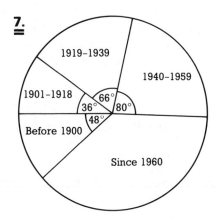

This pie chart shows the periods when the 180 houses in a village were built.

a) What fraction were built before 1940?

b) How many houses have been built since 1960?

c) How many more houses were built from 1940 to 1959 than from 1919 to 1939?

DRAWING PIE CHARTS

If we wish to draw pie charts we need to know the angle at the centre of the circle for each slice.

The table shows the number of items in a twenty-four piece tea set.

Pieces	Plates	Cups	Saucers	Other pieces
Number	7	6	6	5

The plates form $\frac{7}{24}$ of the number of pieces so the angle is $\frac{7}{24}$ of a complete turn, i.e. $\frac{7}{24} \times 360° = 105°$

The angle for the cups is $\frac{6}{24} \times 360° = 90°$

The angle for the saucers also is 90°

The angle for the other pieces is $\frac{5}{24} \times 360° = 75°$

To check the calculation we add the angles. The total should be 360°

Now draw a circle of radius 5 cm and draw one radius.

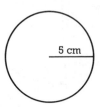

Use your protractor to draw slices of 105°, 90°, and 90°, turning the page to a suitable position to do so. The slice left should measure 75°. Label the pie chart as in previous examples.

EXERCISE 17g Draw pie charts to represent the following information. Work out the angles first.

1. In a class of 30, the eye colours of the pupils were recorded as follows.

Eye colour	Grey	Blue	Brown	Hazel
Frequency	8	4	14	4

2. In a class of 30, the means of transport for coming to school on a given day were recorded as follows.

Means of transport	Bus	Car	Bicycle	Walking	Other
Frequency	12	7	3	5	3

3. In a weekly timetable of 36 periods the distribution of time is as follows.

Subjects	Science, Maths	Art, Music	English	Languages	Others
Frequency	9	6	4	6	11

4. The times spent by the pupils in one form watching different types of television programme one evening were recorded. What was the total viewing time?

Type of programme	Comedy series	News	Plays and films	Docu- mentaries	Other
Time (hours)	15	1	5	5	4

5. A group of 40 people were asked to name the sport they most enjoyed watching.

Sport	Soccer	Tennis	Cricket	Snooker	Other sports
Frequency	12	8	10	6	4

SCATTER GRAPHS

"Tall people have larger feet than shorter people."

This is a fairly obvious statement, but how true is it?

Does it mean, for example, that if my friend and I are the same height, we take the same size in shoes?

Or is there not much truth in the statement, i.e. there is not much relationship between a person's height and their shoe size?

We can try to find out the real situation by gathering some evidence.

This table lists the heights (in centimetres) and the shoe sizes of 12 people (all female).

Height (cm)	158	160	161	163	164	166	166	167	168	170	171	174
Shoe size (continental)	37	36	38	39	37	40	38	37	39	42	41	40

The heights are listed in increasing order. We can see from the table that shoe size does tend to get larger as height increases. However, the tallest person has not got the largest feet so there is not a direct relation between height and shoe size.

We get a clearer picture if we plot these points on a graph.

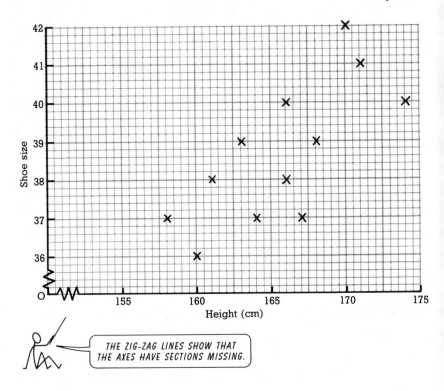

The points do not all fit on a straight line. A graph like this is called a *scatter graph*.

Now we can see that taller people *tend* to have larger feet but the relationship between height and shoe size is not strong enough to justify the original statement.

EXERCISE 17h 1. The table gives the French mark and the maths mark of each of 20 pupils in an end of term examination.

French	45 56 58 58 59 60 64 64 65 65 66 70 71 73 73 75 76 76 78 80
Maths	50 38 45 48 56 65 60 58 70 75 60 79 64 80 85 69 82 77 69 75

a) Show this information on a graph; use a scale of 1 cm for 5 marks on each axis and mark the horizontal axis from 40 to 85 for the French mark and the vertical axis from 35 to 90 for the maths mark.

b) John is good at French. Is he likely to be good at maths?

2. This table shows the heights and weights of 12 people.

Height (cm)	150	152	155	158	158	160	163	165	170	175	178	180
Weight (kg)	56	62	63	64	57	62	65	66	65	70	66	67

a) Show this information on a graph; use a horizontal scale of 2 cm for each 5 cm of height and mark this axis from 145 to 185. Use a vertical scale of 2 cm for each 5 kg and mark this axis from 55 to 75.

b) Carlos weighs 65 kg. Is he likely to be tall?

3. This table shows the number of rooms and the number of people living in each of 15 houses.

Number of rooms	3	4	4	5	5	5	6	6	6	6	7	7	7	8	8
Number of people	2	3	5	4	2	1	6	2	3	4	4	5	3	2	6

a) Show this information by plotting the points on a graph; use a scale of 1 cm for one unit on each axis.

b) Cheryl lives in a house with four other people. Is the house likely to have more than four rooms?

4. This table shows the number of pens and pencils and the number of books that each of 10 pupils have with them in a maths lesson.

Number of pens and pencils	2	3	3	5	6	6	12	15	20	25
Number of books	4	5	0	3	1	4	6	2	1	5

a) Show this information by plotting the points on a graph; use a horizontal scale of 1 cm for two pens and pencils and a vertical scale of 1 cm for one book.

b) Is the number of pens and pencils that one pupil has with them a reliable indication of the number of books that they have with them?

c) Collect the same information for the pupils in your maths class and make a scatter graph from it.

LINE OF BEST FIT AND CORRELATION

If we look again at the scatter graph of height and shoe size, we see that the points are scattered about a straight line which we can draw by eye. This is called *the line of best fit*. When drawing this line the aim is to get the points evenly distributed about the line, so that the sum of the distances from the line of the points that are above it is roughly equal to the sum of the distances from the line of the points that are below it. This may mean that none of the points lie on the line.

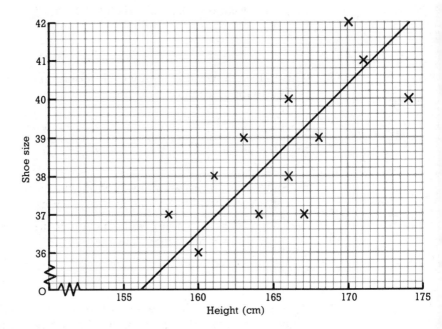

The less scatter there is about the line, the stronger is the relationship between the two quantities. We use the word *correlation* for the relationship between the two quantities.

If the points are close to the line, we say that there is a strong correlation.

If the points are loosely scattered about a line, we say that there is a moderate correlation.

Sometimes the points are so scattered that there is no obvious line and we say that there is no correlation.

EXERCISE 17i **1.** Use the scatter graphs that you drew for Exercise 17h. For each one, draw the line of best fit, if you think there is one. Describe the correlation between the two quantities in each case as 'strong', 'moderate', 'weak' or 'none'.

2. Gather your own evidence on the heights and weights of a group of people. Draw a scatter graph and give an indication of the correlation between a person's height and weight.

18 RATIO

COMPARING SIZES OF QUANTITIES

If we have two quantities, such as 10 cm and 5 cm, we can compare their size in the following way,

10 cm compared with 5 cm is the same as 2 compared with 1.

If the two quantities are 12 g and 8 g then,

because $\qquad$ 12 g $= 3 \times 4$ g

and $\qquad$ 8 g $= 2 \times 4$ g

we can say

12 g compared with 8 g is the same as 3 compared with 2.

EXERCISE 18a

> Compare 20 m with 16 m as simply as possible.
>
> 20 m $= 5 \times 4$ m and 16 m $= 4 \times 4$ m
>
> so 20 m compared with 16 m is the same as 5 compared with 4.

Give the answers to the following questions as simply as possible.

1. Compare £10 with £2.

2. Compare 8 m with 6 m.

3. Compare 15 kg with 10 kg.

4. Compare 36 p with 12 p.

5. Compare 24 g with 18 g.

6. Compare 40 m with 24 m.

To save some of this writing we need a symbol that means "compared with". This symbol is :

10 cm compared with 5 cm is the same as 2 compared with 1

can be written   10 cm : 5 cm = 2 : 1

EXERCISE 18b Rewrite the following sentences using symbols.

1. 10 cm compared with 6 cm is the same as 5 compared with 3.

2. 15 p compared with 5 p is the same as 3 compared with 1.

3. £24 compared with £12 is the same as 2 compared with 1.

4. 72 cm compared with 27 cm is the same as 8 compared with 3.

5. 8 kg compared with 14 kg is the same as 4 compared with 7.

6. Rewrite your sentences from Exercise 18a using symbols.

Write the following statements in words.

7. £18 : £12 = 3 : 2   **9.** 16 cm : 24 cm = 2 : 3

8. 42 cm : 28 cm = 3 : 2   **10.** 18 g : 20 g = 9 : 10

RATIO

We already know that 3 : 2 means "3 compared with 2".
Another way of expressing 3 : 2 is "the ratio 3 to 2"
i.e.   "the ratio 3 to 2" means "3 compared with 2"

SIMPLIFYING RATIOS

We know that 10 cm : 5 cm = 2 : 1. We can see that when both numbers of the ratio 10 : 5 are divided by 5 we get 2 : 1, so a ratio can be simplified if both parts are divided by the same number.

EXERCISE 18c

> Simplify the ratio 20 : 15
>
> 20 : 15 = 4 : 3 (dividing each number by 5)

Simplify the ratio

1. 8 : 10	**5.** 70 : 50	**9.** 27 : 18
2. 6 : 12	**6.** 18 : 6	**10.** 15 : 10
3. 16 : 8	**7.** 24 : 20	**11.** 12 : 9
4. 6 : 9	**8.** 21 : 28	**12.** 8 : 18

Sometimes two or more divisions are needed.

> Simplify the ratio 105 : 75
>
> 105 : 75 = 21 : 15 (dividing each number by 5)
>   = 7 : 5 (dividing each number by 3)

Simplify the ratio

13. 48 : 64	**17.** 64 : 144	**21.** 18 : 108
14. 72 : 168	**18.** 32 : 48	**22.** 175 : 200
15. 108 : 72	**19.** 75 : 120	**23.** 32 : 80
16. 270 : 150	**20.** 28 : 42	**24.** 288 : 120

> Simplify the ratio 18 m : 3 m
>
> (The units are the same for both parts)
> 18 m : 3 m = 18 : 3
>   = 6 : 1

Simplify the ratio

25. 16 cm : 48 cm   **27.** 44 g : 55 g   **29.** 72 kg : 36 kg

26. 20 p : 32 p   **28.** £25 : £15   **30.** 4 mm : 10 mm

EXERCISE 18d

> Simplify the ratio   180 cm : 2 m
>
> (The units must be the same so first change 2 m into cm.)
>
> $\quad$ 2 m $= 2 \times 100$ cm $= 200$ cm
>
> $\quad$ 180 cm : 2 m $= 180$ cm : 200 cm
>
> $\qquad\qquad\qquad = 18 : 20 \quad$ (dividing by 10)
>
> $\qquad\qquad\qquad = \ \ 9 : 10 \quad$ (dividing by 2)

Simplify the following ratios. If the units are not the same, change the larger unit to the smaller unit.

1. 450 cm : 3 m   **7.** 6 cm : 90 mm

2. £2 : 75 p   **8.** £3.25 : 125 p

3. 16 mm : 2 cm   **9.** 90 p : £1.10

4. £2.40 : 48 p   **10.** 25 m : 1000 cm

5. 1 m : 25 cm   **11.** 35 cm : 5 mm

6. 250 m : 0.5 km   **12.** £14 : 70 p

In questions 13 to 16, several alternative answers are given. Write down the letter that corresponds to the correct answer.

13. 5 mm : 3 cm is the same as

$\quad$ **A** 5 : 3 $\qquad$ **B** 1 : 6 $\qquad$ **C** 50 : 3 $\qquad$ **D** 1 : 15

14. 24 p : £1 is the same as

$\quad$ **A** 6 : 100 $\qquad$ **B** 24 : 1 $\qquad$ **C** 25 : 6 $\qquad$ **D** 6 : 25

15. 30 cm : 2 m is the same as

$\quad$ **A** 30 : 2 $\qquad$ **B** 3 : 2 $\qquad$ **C** 3 : 20 $\qquad$ **D** 3 : 200

16. 16 kg : 32 g is the same as

    A 50 : 1   **B** 1 : 2000   **C** 1 : 2   **D** 500 : 1

PROBLEMS

EXERCISE 18e

In a packet of 12 ball-point pens, there are 2 red ones and the rest are blue. What is the ratio of the number of blue pens to the number of red pens?

There are 10 blue and 2 red pens.

    Therefore the ratio of blue to red is 10 : 2

                         = 5 : 1

1. Peter is 16 years old and Anne is 12 years old. What is the ratio of Peter's age to Anne's age?

2. The pupils in a class own 16 pets between them. If 10 of the pets are dogs, what is the ratio of the number of dogs to the number of other animals?

3. Pat has 9 exercise books on her desk. If 3 are brown and the rest are green, what is the ratio of the number of brown books to the number of green books?

4. In a class of 24, there are 15 boys. What is the ratio of the number of girls to the number of boys?

5. Of 22 vehicles parked in a road, 6 are vans. What is the ratio of the number of vans to the number of other vehicles?

6. Driving the 120 miles from Abbotsford to Barford, I cover 96 miles on motorways. What is the ratio of the number of miles driven on motorways to the number of miles on other roads?

7. A farm of 200 hectares uses 125 hectares for growing cereals and the rest for grazing. What is the ratio of the number of hectares used for growing cereals to the number of hectares used for grazing?

8. On a day out Mr Jones spends £6.50 on tickets and £7.50 on food. What is the ratio of the amount spent on food to the amount spent on tickets?

DIVISION IN A GIVEN RATIO

If we are asked to divide a length of 5 cm into two parts so that the ratio of the lengths of the two parts is 2 : 3, it is easy to see that the two lengths must be 2 cm and 3 cm.

Now suppose that the length to be divided is 40 cm. We want the ratio of the two parts to be 2 : 3, so one part is made up of 2 portions and the other of 3 portions, i.e. there are 5 portions altogether.

Dividing the 40 cm length into 5 equal portions gives the length of one portion as $\frac{40}{5}$ cm, i.e. 8 cm,

so the length of the first part $= 2 \times 8$ cm

                                          $= 16$ cm

and the length of the second part $= 3 \times 8$ cm

                                          $= 24$ cm

(We can check by adding the two lengths, i.e. 24 cm + 16 cm $=$ 40 cm)

EXERCISE 18f

Divide 60 kg into two parts in the ratio 7 : 5

There are $(7 + 5)$ portions, i.e. 12 portions

1 portion $= \frac{60}{12}$ kg

                  $= 5$ kg

First part $= 7 \times 5$ kg

                  $= 35$ kg

Second part $= 5 \times 5$ kg

                  $= 25$ kg

(Check   25 kg + 35 kg $=$ 60 kg)

1. Divide 60 cm into two parts in the ratio 5 : 1

2. Divide 90 p into two parts in the ratio 4 : 5

3. Divide 72 m into two parts in the ratio 2 : 7

4. Divide 18 kg into two parts in the ratio 1 : 2

5. Divide 14 m into two parts in the ratio 3 : 4

6. Divide 24 cm into two parts in the ratio 3 : 1

7. Divide 80 p between Eleanor and Mary in the ratio 5 : 3

8. Divide £1.20 between two people in the ratio 5 : 7

9. Divide 108 km into two parts in the ratio 1 : 8

10. Share 40 sweets between two people in the ratio 2 : 3

11. John is 18 years old and James is 15 years old. Share 66 p between them in the ratio of their ages.

In questions 12 and 13, several alternative answers are given. Write down the letter that corresponds to the correct answer.

12. When 20 cm is divided into two parts in the ratio 4 : 1, the two parts are

A 5 cm, 1 cm   C 4 cm, 1 cm
B 15 cm, 5 cm   D 16 cm, 4 cm

13. When 24 g is divided into two parts in the ratio 3 : 5, the two parts are

A 3 g, 5 g   B 24 g, 40 g   C 15 g, 9 g   D 9 g, 15 g

MAP SCALES

On a map let us suppose that 1 cm represents 1 km. Then the ratio of the distance on the map to the distance on the ground, i.e. the *real* distance, is 1 cm : 1 km.

$$\text{Now, } 1 \text{ km} = 1000 \text{ m}$$
$$= 100\,000 \text{ cm}$$
$$\text{so } 1 \text{ cm} : 1 \text{ km} = 1 \text{ cm} : 100\,000 \text{ cm}$$
$$= 1 : 100\,000$$

For this map, we say that the *map scale* or map ratio is 1 : 100 000.

On the cover of some Ordnance Survey maps you will find the ratio 1 : 50 000. This means that 1 cm represents 50 000 cm

i.e.   1 cm represents $\frac{1}{2}$ km.

EXERCISE 18g

On a road atlas the map ratio is 1 : 200 000. What real distance is represented by 1 cm on the map? Give your answer in kilometres.

The map ratio is 1 : 200 000

so 1 cm represents 200 000 cm

$$= \frac{200\,000}{100} \text{ m} \qquad (100 \text{ cm} = 1 \text{ m})$$

$$= 2000 \text{ m}$$

$$= \frac{2000}{1000} \text{ km} \qquad (1000 \text{ m} = 1 \text{ km})$$

$$= 2 \text{ km}$$

1. A map ratio is 1 : 5000. What real distance in metres is represented by 1 cm on the map?

2. A map ratio is 1 : 10 000. What real distance in metres is represented by 1 cm on the map?

3. A map ratio is 1 : 10 000 000. What real distance in kilometres is represented by 1 cm on the map?

4. A map ratio is 1 : 20 000. What distance in metres is represented by 1 cm on the map?

A map ratio is 1 : 10 000. What real distance in kilometres is represented by 5 cm on the map?

1 cm represents 10 000 cm

5 cm represents 50 000 cm

= 500 m

= $\frac{1}{2}$ km

---

5. The ratio marked on a map is 1 : 5000. What real distance in metres is represented by 10 cm on the map?

6. A map ratio is 1 : 100 000. What real distance in kilometres is represented by 6 cm on the map?

7. The ratio on an Ordnance Survey map is 1 : 50 000. What distance in kilometres is represented by 12 cm on the map?

8. On a street map of a town, the ratio is given as 1 : 1000. What distance is represented by 8 cm on the map?

9. A map ratio is 1 : 1 000 000. What distance in kilometres is represented by 8 cm on the map?

10. Use the map given in the worked example opposite to find the straight line distance between
   a) Batley and Daxton
   b) Capminster and Edgewood
   c) Althorpe and Batley
   d) Capminster and Devil's Rock

This map shows the positions of five towns. The map ratio is 1 : 100 000. Find the straight line distance between Althorpe and Daxton.

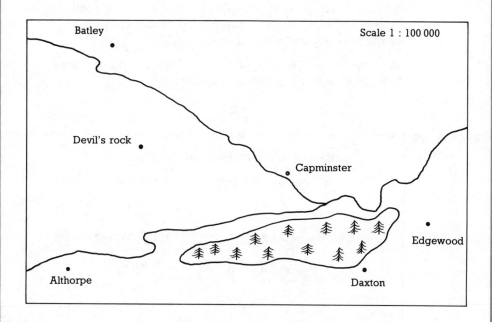

The map ratio is 1 : 100 000

so 1 cm represents 100 000 cm

$$= \frac{100\,000}{100} \text{ m} \qquad (100 \text{ cm} = 1 \text{ m})$$

$$= 1000 \text{ m}$$

$$= \frac{1000}{1000} \text{ km} \qquad (1000 \text{ m} = 1 \text{ km})$$

$$= 1 \text{ km}$$

The straight line distance between Althorpe and Daxton on the map is 8 cm.

Therefore the actual distance between Althorpe and Daxton is 8 × 1 km, i.e. 8 km.

DIRECT PROPORTION

"Proportion" is another word used for comparison. Two quantities are in proportion if they are always in the same ratio, e.g. if one quantity is doubled, so is the other one.

When we buy records at a fixed price each, the total cost of the records is proportional to the number bought, e.g. if we treble the number bought we treble the cost.

As another example, if a plane is flying at a steady speed then the distance travelled is proportional to the time taken.

EXERCISE 18h

The total cost of 5 identical pens is 80 p.

Find   a) the cost of 1 pen   b) the cost of 7 pens.

a) 5 pens cost 80 p   b) 7 pens cost 7×16 p

$\therefore$ 1 pen costs $\frac{80}{5}$ p $= 112$ p

$= 16$ p $= £1.12$

1. Six envelopes cost 54 p. Find
   a) the cost of 1 envelope
   b) the cost of 10 envelopes

2. Four packets of cornflakes, all of equal mass, have a total mass of 2000 g.
   a) What is the mass of 1 packet?
   b) What is the mass of 9 packets?

3. If 8 m of chain costs 240 p, what is the cost of
   a) 1 m?
   b) 5 m?

4. Six labradors, all with equal appetites, eat 24 kg of food in a week.
   a) How much does one labrador eat in a week?
   b) How much do five of these labradors eat in a week?

5. Six men, working at the same rate, dig a trench 24 m long in a day.

a) How long a trench would 1 man dig?
b) How long a trench would 4 men dig?

6. Mr Jones finds he can buy 2 m of dowel for 24 p.

a) What is the cost of 1 m?
b) What is the cost of 5 m?

7. At a steady rate, a man drives 280 km in 4 hours.

a) How far does he drive in 1 hour?
b) How far does he drive in 3 hours?

In questions 8 to 16, you may need to find out about one item, as you did in questions 1 to 7, before completing your answer.

8. Nine pencils cost 72 p. What is the cost of eight pencils?

9. A clock gains 15 minutes in 5 days. How much does it gain in 7 days?

10. At a steady rate, a man drives 72 miles in 2 hours. How far does he drive in 3 hours?

11. Six chairs cost £42. What is the cost of five of these chairs?

12. A clock gains 2 minutes in 6 days. How many days does it take to gain 5 minutes?

13. A carpet of area 12 m^2 costs £96. At the same cost per m^2, what is the cost of a carpet of area 15 m^2?

14. Seven tickets for a concert cost £21. How much would five of these tickets cost?

15. If 3 m of shelving are needed for 135 copies of a text book, how many copies can be put on 5 m of shelving?

16. On 6 pages of printed text there are 2100 words. How many words are there on 8 pages?

Mortar is made by mixing sand and cement in the ratio 3 : 1.

a) How much cement would be needed to mix with 18 tons of sand?

b) How much sand would be required to mix with 30 kg of cement?

a) 3 tons of sand is required to mix with 1 ton of cement

1 ton of sand is required to mix with $\frac{1}{3}$ ton of cement

18 tons of sand is required to mix with $18 \times \frac{1}{3}$ tons of cement

i.e. 6 tons of cement

b) If the ratio of sand to cement is 3 : 1

the ratio of cement to sand is 1 : 3

i.e. 1 kg of cement would need 3 kg of sand

so 30 kg of cement would need 3×30 kg of sand

i.e. 90 kg of sand

17. Mortar is made by mixing sand and cement in the ratio 3 : 1.

a) How much cement would be needed to mix with 15 tons of sand?

b) How much sand would be needed to mix with 70 kg of cement?

18. A recipe for swiss roll includes 100 g of margarine, 4 large eggs and 250 g of caster sugar. If a larger swiss roll is made

a) how many eggs would be needed to mix with 500 g of margarine?

b) how much margarine would be needed to mix with 1000 g of caster sugar?

c) how much margarine would be needed to mix with a dozen eggs?

19. An alloy is made by mixing copper and zinc in the ratio 1 : 5.
   a) How much zinc is needed to mix with 30 tons of copper?
   b) How much copper is needed to mix with 100 tons of zinc?

20. A recipe for a cake to serve six people includes 3 oz of sugar, 6 oz of plain flour and 3 eggs. Dave buys half a dozen eggs and intends to use them all to make one large cake.
   a) How much sugar does he need?
   b) How much plain flour does he need?
   c) How many people should he be able to serve?

MIXED EXERCISES

EXERCISE 18i 1. Simplify the ratio 15 : 3

2. Simplify the ratio 36 : 54

3. Fill the gap in the ratio   10 : 8 = 5 :

4. Divide 60 cm into two parts in the ratio 2 : 3

5. Mr and Mrs Lark have 6 grandsons and 4 granddaughters. Find the ratio of the number of grandsons to the number of granddaughters.

6. A map ratio is 1 : 10 000. Find the real distance in metres represented by 1 cm on the map.

7. Three men, working at the same rate, build 15 m of wall. In the same time, how many metres of the wall would two men build?

EXERCISE 18j 1. Simplify the ratio 4 : 16

2. Simplify the ratio 36 : 30

3. Fill the gap in the ratio   6 : 5 =   : 15

4. Divide 72 p into two parts in the ratio 7 : 2

5. John is 7 years old and Alan is 9 years old. Divide 80 p between them in the ratio of their ages.

6. An Ordnance Survey map is marked with the ratio 1 : 500 000. What distance in kilometres is represented by 7 cm on the map?

7. At a steady speed, a motorist drives 120 km in 3 hours. At the same speed, how far does he go in 5 hours?

EXERCISE 18k In the following questions, several alternative answers are given. Write down the letter that corresponds to the correct answer.

1. The ratio 24 : 16 is the same as

    A 3 : 2   **B** 2 : 3   **C** 2 : 1   **D** 1 : 3

2. When 36 p is divided into two parts in the ratio 7 : 2, the larger part is

    A 7 p   **B** 28 p   **C** 8 p   **D** 14 p

3. In a class of 30 pupils, 16 are boys. The ratio of boys to girls is

    A 8 : 7   **B** 8 : 15   **C** 15 : 8   **D** 7 : 8

4. A map ratio is 1 : 5000. The distance represented by 10 cm on the map is

    A 10 km   **B** 1 km   **C** 5000 m   **D** 500 m

19 INDICES AND SIGNIFICANT FIGURES

THE MEANING OF INDEX NUMBERS

We have seen in Chapter 1 that 5^2 means 5×5
Similarly, 5^4 means $5 \times 5 \times 5 \times 5$ and we say "five to the fourth power" or "five to the fourth" or "five to the four" for short.

EXERCISE 19a

Find the value of 3^4

$$3^4 = 3 \times 3 \times 3 \times 3$$
$$= 81$$

Find the value of

1. 2^3 **3.** 5^3 **5.** 2^4

2. 3^2 **4.** 4^1 **6.** 2^7

Write in index form

7. 6×6 **9.** 3 **11.** $7 \times 7 \times 7 \times 7$

8. $2 \times 2 \times 2 \times 2 \times 2$ **10.** 4×4 **12.** $7 \times 7 \times 7$

Find the value in index form of
a) $2^2 \times 2^4$ b) $2^5 \div 2^2$

a) $2^2 \times 2^4 = 2 \times 2 \times 2 \times 2 \times 2 \times 2$
$$= 2^6$$

b) $2^5 \div 2^2 = \dfrac{2 \times 2 \times 2 \times \cancel{2} \times \cancel{2}}{\cancel{2} \times \cancel{2}}$
$$= 2^3$$

Find in index form

13. $2^3 \times 2^5$ **16.** $7^6 \div 7^2$ **19.** $5^3 \times 5^4$

14. $3^2 \times 3^3$ **17.** $3^4 \div 3^2$ **20.** $2^8 \div 2^3$

15. $5^4 \times 5^1$ **18.** 2×2^3 **21.** $2^3 \div 2^2$

22. What do you notice about the given index numbers and the answers in questions 13, 14 and 15?

23. What do you notice about the given index numbers and the answers in questions 16, 17 and 20?

RULES OF INDICES

We can see from the last exercise that to multiply numbers in index form we *add* the index numbers.

> To multiply powers of the *same* number we add the index numbers.

Notice that $2^2 \times 3^4$ cannot be simplified by this rule because 3 is different from 2.

To divide numbers in index form we see from the last exercise that we *subtract* the index numbers.

> To divide powers of the *same* number we subtract the second index number from the first.

EXERCISE 19b Write as a single number in index form

1. $2^3 \times 2^4$ **6.** $5^8 \div 5^4$ **11.** $3^6 \times 3$

2. $3^2 \times 3^3$ **7.** $3^7 \times 3^2$ **12.** $3^6 \div 3$

3. $2^2 \times 2^4$ **8.** $2^5 \div 2^4$ **13.** $2^7 \times 2^3$

4. $2^7 \div 2^3$ **9.** $7^2 \times 7^4$ **14.** $6^2 \times 6^4$

5. $4^5 \div 4^3$ **10.** $5^6 \div 5^1$ **15.** $6^4 \times 6^2$

If you have a scientific calculator, you can make use of the index button to work out the value of, say, 2^4.

The button is usually marked $\boxed{x^y}$ (but may be $\boxed{y^x}$ or $\boxed{a^x}$)

Press $\boxed{2}$ $\boxed{x^y}$ $\boxed{4}$ $\boxed{=}$ and you will see 16 on the display.

16. Work out the value of each of the following numbers
   a) 2^7 b) 3^5 c) 5^4 d) 4^3

17. Work out the value of $5^3 \times 5^2$

18. Is it possible to write $2^3 \times 3^2$ as a single number in index form? If not, why not?

USING LETTERS

The index rules hold for letters as well as for numbers.

EXERCISE 19c

Simplify   a) $x^3 \times x^4$ b) $y^6 \div y^2$ c) $x^4 \times y^2$

a) $x^3 \times x^4 = x^7$

b) $y^6 \div y^2 = y^4$

c) $x^4 \times y^2 = x^4 y^2$  THIS CANNOT BE SIMPLIFIED.

Simplify if possible

1. $x^6 \times x^2$ **4.** $z^4 \times z^2$ **7.** $y^6 \times y$

2. $x^6 \div x^2$ **5.** $x^3 \times x^6$ **8.** $y^6 \div x^2$

3. $y^6 \times x^2$ **6.** $x^6 \div x^3$ **9.** $y^6 \times y^2$

Simplify $4x^3 \times 3x^2$

(Multiply the numbers first, then the letters.)

$4x^3 \times 3x^2 = 4 \times x^3 \times 3 \times x^2$

$= 12 \times x^5$

$= 12x^5$

Simplify

10. $2x^2 \times 3x^3$

13. $12y^6 \times 3y^2$

16. $2z^5 \times 2z^5$

11. $4a^3 \times 2a^5$

14. $4x^2 \times 5x$

17. $5x^2 \times x^3$

12. $6s^4 \times 2s^2$

15. $7c^4 \times 2c^3$

18. $x^2 \times 4x$

Simplify $x^2 \times x^3 \times x$

$x^2 \times x^3 \times x = x^{2+3+1}$

$= x^6$

Simplify

19. $x^4 \times x^3 \times x$

20. $y^2 \times y^2 \times y^2$

21. $z \times z^6 \times z^2$

Simplify $(x^2)^3$

$(x^2)^3 = x^2 \times x^2 \times x^2$

$= x^{2+2+2}$

$= x^6$

Simplify

22. $(x^3)^2$ **24.** $(y^3)^3$ **26.** $(a^3)^4$

23. $(y^4)^2$ **25.** $(a^4)^3$ **27.** $(a^4)^2$

STANDARD FORM

Very large numbers can be written more conveniently in standard form. They take up less space and it is easier to compare sizes.

A number in standard form is written as a number between 1 and 10 multiplied by the appropriate power of 10.

We can write 1500 as 1.5×1000, i.e. as 1.5×10^3

Notice however that 1.5×10^3 is in standard form but 15×10^2 is not.

EXERCISE 19d

3.2×10^4 is written in standard form. Write it as an ordinary number.

$$3.2 \times 10^4 = 3.2 \times 10\,000$$
$$= 32\,000$$

Write as ordinary numbers

1. 3.6×10^2 **4.** 2.65×10^4 **7.** 7.2×10^6

2. 6.3×10^4 **5.** 4.88×10^2 **8.** 4.789×10^2

3. 9.1×10^3 **6.** 5.44×10^1 **9.** 5.3×10^8

Write the numbers in each of the following statements as ordinary numbers.

10. The distance from the Earth to the Moon is 3.8×10^5 km.

11. Sound travels at 3.3×10^2 metres per second.

12. The greatest distance of the Earth from the Sun is 1.52×10^8 km.

13. The diameter of the Earth is 1.2756×10^4 km.

USING A SCIENTIFIC CALCULATOR ━━━━━━━━━━━━━━━━━━

If you have a scientific calculator it will display very large or very small numbers in standard form (scientific notation).
However, only the power of 10 is shown; 10 itself does not appear on the display.

Suppose you wish to find the square of 500 000.

Enter 500 000 in your calculator $\boxed{5}\,\boxed{0}\,\boxed{0}\,\boxed{0}\,\boxed{0}\,\boxed{0}$

If we want to square this number, the buttons we would press on various calculators could be

$$\boxed{x^2} \quad \text{or} \quad \boxed{\text{INV}}\,\boxed{\sqrt{x}} \quad \text{or} \quad \boxed{\text{INV}}\,\boxed{\sqrt{}}$$

The display will read $\boxed{2.5 \quad 11}$ or $\boxed{2.5 \quad ^{11}}$

This means 2.5×10^{11}

So $(500\,000)^2 = 2.5 \times 100\,000\,000\,000$

                              $= 250\,000\,000\,000$

EXERCISE 19e

Calculate $360\,000 \times 24\,000\,000$

$(\text{Press}\quad \boxed{3}\,\boxed{6}\,\boxed{0}\,\boxed{0}\,\boxed{0}\,\boxed{0}$

$\boxed{\times}\,\boxed{2}\,\boxed{4}\,\boxed{0}\,\boxed{0}\,\boxed{0}\,\boxed{0}\,\boxed{0}\,\boxed{0}\,\boxed{=}$

The display will show $\boxed{8.64 \quad 12}$ $)$

$360\,000 \times 24\,000\,000 = 8.64 \times 10^{12}$

$= 8.64 \times 1\,000\,000\,000\,000$

$= 8\,640\,000\,000\,000$

Use your calculator to find each of the following numbers
a) in standard form   b) as an ordinary number.

1. $300\,000 \times 400\,000$

2. $460\,000\,000 \times 230$

3. $45\,000\,000 \times 40\,000\,000$

4. $458\,000\,000 \times 4\,500\,000$

5. $3\,600\,000 \times 6\,000\,000\,000$

6. $320\,000 \times 4\,500\,000\,000$

If the numbers you are using are very small, then the calculator display will show a negative index number and you will have to *divide* by powers of 10 instead of multiplying.

Calculate   a) $0.0004 \div 20\,000\,000$ b) $0.004 \div 20$

a) $\Big($ Press $\boxed{\cdot}\;\boxed{0}\;\boxed{0}\;\boxed{0}\;\boxed{4}$

  $\boxed{\div}\;\boxed{2}\;\boxed{0}\;\boxed{0}\;\boxed{0}\;\boxed{0}\;\boxed{0}\;\boxed{0}\;\boxed{0}\;\boxed{=}$

and the display will show $\boxed{2 \quad -11}$

This means 2×10^{-11} $\Big)$

$$0.0004 \div 20\,000\,000 = 2 \div 10^{11}$$
$$= 2 \div 100\,000\,000\,000$$
$$= 0.000\,000\,000\,02$$

b) $\Big($ Press $\boxed{\cdot}\;\boxed{0}\;\boxed{0}\;\boxed{4}\;\boxed{\div}\;\boxed{2}\;\boxed{0}\;\boxed{=}$ and the

display will show $\boxed{2 \quad -04}$.

The display always shows the index number as a two-figure number so it fills in with a 0 before the 4.$\Big)$

$$0.004 \div 20 = 2 \div 10^{4}$$
$$= 2 \div 10\,000$$
$$= 0.0002$$

Find

7. $0.000\,65 \times 0.0004$

8. 0.0023×0.0005

9. $0.005 \div 2$

10. $0.0048 \div 32$

11. $(0.0044)^{2}$

12. 0.008×0.002

SIGNIFICANT FIGURES

If you were asked to measure the width of a table correct to one decimal place and you chose to use metres, your answer might be 0.8 metres. However if you chose to use centimetres, your answer might be 75.3 cm, which is more accurate than the answer in metres.

Therefore asking for a figure to be given correct to a certain number of decimal places is not always practical.

If you were asked for the width of the table correct to the first three digits, then your answer might be   0.753 m
or   75.3 cm
or   753 mm

In all three cases we have the same degree of accuracy, i.e. the measurement is correct to the nearest millimetre, and we say that we have given the answer correct to *three significant figures*.

To correct to, say, 2 significant figures, we look at the next significant figure: if this is 5 or more we add 1 to the previous figure, as we do with decimal places. If it is less than 5 we do not alter the previous figure.

EXERCISE 19f

Write down the third significant figure in the number 73.82 and state what it represents.

73.<u>8</u>2

The 3rd s.f. is 8 and it represents 8 tenths.

1. Write down the 2nd significant figure in each number and say what it represents.

   a) 32.6   b) 6.789   c) 3567

2. Write down the 3rd significant figure in each number and say what it represents.

a) 45 210   b) 45.89   c) 6.782

3. Write down the 1st significant figure in each number and say what it represents.

a) 412   b) 0.31   c) 3.68

Write down the 2nd significant figure in each of the following numbers and state what it represents.

a) 3045   b) 0.0785

a) 3045

(The 0 counts as a significant figure if it is between other figures.)

The 2nd significant figure is 0 so there are no hundreds.

b) 0.0785

(0's *before* other figures do not count as significant figures.)

The 2nd significant figure is 8 and it represents 8 thousandths.

---

4. Write down the 3rd significant figure in each number and state what it represents.

a) 3046   b) 57 055   c) 0.0673

5. Write down the 2nd significant figure in each number and state what it represents.

a) 6.045   b) 0.0349   c) 0.087 62

6. Write down the 4th significant figure in each number and state what it represents.

a) 4802   b) 0.641 341   c) 0.060 407

Give the following numbers correct to 3 s.f.

a) 89 472   b) 0.089 472   c) 0.4298

a) 894|72 = 89 500 correct to 3 s.f.

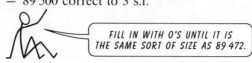

FILL IN WITH 0'S UNTIL IT IS
THE SAME SORT OF SIZE AS 89 472.

b) 0.0894|72 = 0.0895 correct to 3 s.f.

c) 0.429|8 = 0.430 correct to 3 s.f.

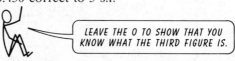

LEAVE THE 0 TO SHOW THAT YOU
KNOW WHAT THE THIRD FIGURE IS.

Give the following numbers correct to 2 s.f.

7. 8.254	**10.** 12.8	**13.** 0.824
8. 4.073	**11.** 172	**14.** 0.0873
9. 2.16	**12.** 43.7	**15.** 0.003 07

Give the following numbers correct to 3 s.f.

16. 9.267	**19.** 86.59	**22.** 0.025 44
17. 6.058	**20.** 759.42	**23.** 0.877 66
18. 4.397	**21.** 3699	**24.** 0.000 509 92

Give each of the following numbers correct to the number of significant figures indicated in brackets.

25. 73.14 (2)	**28.** 70 945 (4)	**31.** 1.2799 (3)
26. 0.057 37 (3)	**29.** 0.009 372 (2)	**32.** 0.788 01 (4)
27. 889.4 (3)	**30.** 3.141 59 (4)	**33.** 0.002 657 (3)

USING A CALCULATOR

Calculators are marvellous aids because they take the drudgery out of many calculations. We cannot always be certain, however, that the answer they give is correct because *we* make mistakes when using them, particularly when we enter numbers. Our mistakes often result in outrageously incorrect answers so we should always ask "Is the answer reasonable?" One way to answer this question is to get a rough idea of the size of answer we expect. We can do this by correcting each number in the calculation to one significant figure and then working out the rough answer.

For example $25.738 \times 9.837 \approx 30 \times 10 = 300$

On a calculator $25.738 \times 9.837 = 253.18471$

This is the same sort of size as the rough estimate, so it is probably correct.

If we want an answer correct to 3 significant figures, we usually see more figures on the display than we need to answer the question.

In this case we see   253.18471

We write down the first 4 figures (one more than we are asked for) and then give the answer correct to 3 s.f.

So $25.738 \times 9.837 = 253.1 \ldots$

$$= 253 \text{ correct to 3 s.f.}$$

EXERCISE 19g

a) Calculate 82.49×0.7326 giving the answer correct to 3 s.f.
b) Calculate 427×59.2 giving the answer correct to 2 s.f.

a) Rough estimate: $80 \times 0.7 = 56.0$

$$82.49 \times 0.7326 = 60.4\,|3 \ldots$$

$$= 60.4 \text{ correct to 3 s.f.}$$

b) Rough estimate: $400 \times 60 = 24\,000$

$$427 \times 59.2 = 25\,|2 \ldots$$

KEEP AN EYE ON THE ROUGH ESTIMATE. WE NEED TO ADD THREE 0'S TO MAKE THE NUMBER THE RIGHT SIZE.

$$= 25\,000 \text{ correct to 2 s.f.}$$

First give a rough estimate for each of the following calculations, then use your calculator and give your answer correct to 3 s.f.

1. 27.8×5.243 **6.** 8.99×4.06

2. $57.2 \div 2.9$ **7.** $278 \div 27.3$

3. 8.742×0.2015 **8.** $26.9 \div 5.37$

4. $604 \div 58.2$ **9.** 67.3×0.92

5. 13.6×25.2 **10.** $55.5 \div 1.66$

11. Find the area of a rectangle measuring 34.2 cm by 47.3 cm.

12. Find the total mass of 16 boxes each of mass 14.8 kg.

13. Each fence post takes up a space of 24.5 cm. What space will 19 fence posts need?

14. Find the value of $x \div y$ if $x = 4.5$ and $y = 2.1$.

15. Find the square of 567.

MIXED EXERCISES

EXERCISE 19h   **1.** Find the value of $4^2 \times 3^3$

2. Give in index form $3^5 \div 3^3$

3. Simplify $4x^4 \times 3x^2$

4. Write 4.67×10^4 as an ordinary number and then give it correct to 2 s.f.

5. On a shelf, seven books of the same size take up 22 cm. How wide is each book? Give your answer correct to 3 s.f.

EXERCISE 19i In this exercise you are given several alternative answers. Write down the letter that corresponds to the correct answer.

1. The second significant figure of 825.34 represents

   A 2 hundreds   **B** 5 units   **C** 2 tens   **D** 4 tenths

2. Correct to two significant figures, the value of 0.796 is

    A 1.0   **B** 0.79   **C** 0.8   **D** 0.80

3. The value of $2^2 \times 2^3$ is

    A 64   **B** $\frac{1}{2}$ **C** 32   **D** 8

4. $(4^2)^3$ is

    A 4^5 **B** 4^6 **C** 4^8 **D** 8^3

5. A rough answer for 0.29×5.7 is

    A 1.8   **B** 0.2   **C** 0.3   **D** 6

6. $4^6 \div 4^2$ can be written as

    A 4^8 **B** 4^3 **C** 4^4 **D** 3

20 COLLECTING INFORMATION

DECIDING HOW TO COLLECT INFORMATION

Up to now you have been given information about, for example, the heights of a group of people, and you have been asked to sort it out and draw a bar chart.

If you have to collect the information yourself, you need to plan in advance and decide how you are going to solve some of the problems that might arise.

EXERCISE 20a 1. Information about the heights of a group of people was collected. It was then sorted in two different ways. In the first case there were 12 different categories with a few entries in each. In the second case there were 6 categories. Below are the two different bar charts drawn using the information.

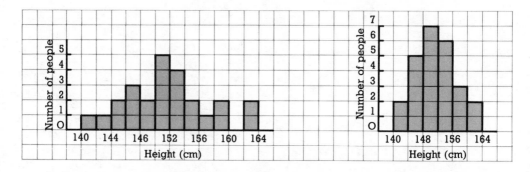

a) Which bar chart do you prefer? Give your reasons.

b) Is it better to have a large number of categories or just a few?

2. Suppose that information is to be collected about the shoe sizes of pupils in your year, and a bar chart is to be drawn using the information.

a) How many categories do you need? Should you stick to whole number sizes?

b) If you decide on whole number sizes, what should you do about a pupil who insists that all her shoes are size $3\frac{1}{2}$?

266

  c) What should you do about someone whose left shoe is size 3 and whose right is size 4?

  d) Some people are shy about giving their shoe size. What can you do about this?

  e) If you ask people to write their shoe sizes on a piece of paper anonymously, what could go wrong?

  f) Can you think of any other problems that might arise when collecting information about shoe sizes?

EXERCISE 20b **1.** Information is to be collected about the heights of pupils in the first year.

You could collect the information by one of the following methods.

A Prepare the frequency table and, as you get the information from a pupil, make a tally mark in the appropriate place.

B Have a list of all the pupils in the year and write the information against the appropriate name.

Which do you think is the more efficient method? Give your reasons.

2. Imagine that you now go out to collect information on heights.

  a) Some people will know their height in feet and inches, others in centimetres. What will you do about this?

  b) What other problems are you likely to encounter?

  c) Suppose that the least height is 151 cm and the greatest height is 168 cm.

   What categories will you use for grouping the information?

3. Information is to be collected about the eye colour of pupils in the first year.

  a) State the categories you would use.

  b) List the problems you are likely to encounter as you collect the information.

4. Choose a topic on which to collect information.

  a) List the categories into which the information is to be put.

  b) Decide whether you will draw a bar chart or a pie chart.

  c) List the difficulties you are likely to encounter in collecting the information and what you will do to get round them.

QUESTIONNAIRES ————————————————————————

The information required sometimes concerns opinion on several different points. For example, you may want to find out whether pupils would prefer an earlier start to the day or a shorter lunch hour. In cases like this a sheet of questions for each person might be more useful.

A set of questions of this sort is called a *questionnaire*.

EXERCISE 20c 1. Copy and complete this questionnaire.
(Notice the different types of question and forms of answer.)

a) How tall are you?   . . . . cm

b) Do you consider yourself to be
Tall   Average   Small
(Underline your answer.)

c) Do you like being the height you are? Underline your answer.
Love it   Like it   Don't mind   Dislike it   Hate it

d) I want to grow taller   0   1   2   3
(0 means "not at all", 3 means "very much")
Ring the number that represents your answer.

e) I am male/female. (Cross out the unwanted word.)

2. a) In the questionnaire above, why is question (e) needed?

b) Question 1(c) could have had an answer in a different form, such as:
2   1   0   −1   −2   Ring the number which represents your liking.
What is the problem when the question is put in this form or as in question 1(d)?

3. There are several things wrong with the wording of the following questions. List them, giving reasons for your choice.

a) Do you like mathematics?   0   1   2   3   4

b) What colour is your hair?   . . . .

c) How many people are there in your family?   . . . .

4. We wish to find out whether or not the following hypothesis is true.
"People with small hands have small feet and people with bigger hands have bigger feet."

a) Decide who you will ask for information about the sizes of their hands and feet. Will you ask friends and relations or pupils in school? Will you ask pupils in your own year or in other years as well? How many people should you collect information from?

b) Decide whether you will ask for shoe size or the length of the foot in cm. (You will have to be prepared to measure feet with a tapemeasure or ruler.)

c) How will you measure hand size? Will you use the length or the span?

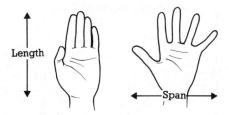

d) Prepare a table with three columns, for name, foot size and hand size.

e) Collect the information.

f) Draw a scatter graph for foot size and hand size.

g) Is there good correlation or none at all?

h) What conclusion do you come to about the hypothesis?

i) Make a frequency table for the foot sizes, using six categories. Draw a bar chart.

j) Make a frequency table for the hand sizes, again using six categories. Draw a bar chart.
(Make sure you have given a title to each bar chart.)

k) Compare the shapes of the two bar charts.

5. Write a questionnaire on a topic of your own choice, using different types of questions. Sometimes the wording can be misunderstood: try the questions out on someone before setting out to collect information.

21 TWO-WAY TABLES AND NETWORKS

TWO-WAY TABLES

Some tables contain entries which can be used only if two pieces of information are known. These are called *two-way tables*.

EXERCISE 21a

The pupils in a class were each asked how many girls and boys there were in their family. This table shows the results of the enquiries.

Number of girls

		0	1	2	3
Number of boys	0	0	4	5	1
	1	3	7	(3)	1
	2	4	4	0	0

a) How many families are there with 2 girls and 1 boy?
b) How many families are there with 3 girls and any number of boys?

a) (Look down the column for 2 girls until you reach the row with 1 boy.)

There are 3 families with 2 girls and 1 boy.

b) (There could be 0, 1 or 2 boys.)

There are $1 + 1 + 0$ families with 3 girls, i.e. 2 families.

1. This question refers to the table in the worked example opposite.

 a) How many families are there with 2 boys and 1 girl?

 b) How many families are there with 1 girl and any number of boys?

 c) How many families are there with at least 1 boy?

 d) How many families are there altogether?

 e) Why must the entry for 0 girls and 0 boys be zero?

2. The pupils in a class were each asked to give their hair and eye colours. This table shows the results.

Eye colour

		Blue	Grey	Dark	Hazel
Hair colour	Dark	1	2	10	2
	Medium	4	2	1	0
	Fair	5	1	0	1
	Red	0	1	0	0

 a) How many pupils have fair hair and grey eyes?

 b) How many pupils have dark hair?

 c) How many pupils are there in the class?

3. A study was made of the number of cars and garages owned by each household in a street. This table shows the results.

Cars

		0	1	2	3
Garages	0	7	5	1	0
	1	3	9	1	0
	2	0	0	1	1

 a) How many households have 2 cars and 2 garages?

 b) How many households have 1 car?

 c) How many households are there altogether in the street?

4. This table shows the various numbers of daily and evening papers taken by the households in one street. There are 32 households altogether and 16 have no evening paper.

Daily paper

		0	1	2
Evening paper	0		9	3
	1	6		1

a) Copy and complete the table.

b) How many households have 2 daily papers and no evening paper?

OTHER TWO-WAY TABLES

Sometimes the entry is not a number but a quantity such as a time or a cost. These tables are more common.

EXERCISE 21b

This table shows the cost of a coach journey from my home town to various places on different days of the week.

	Mon. to Thurs.	Fri.	Sat.	Sun.
London	£4.60	£5.50	£5.80	£4.00
Alton Towers	£3.50	£3.50	£4.50	£5.00
Birmingham	£5.00	£5.00	£5.50	£4.80

a) What is the cost of a journey to Alton Towers on a Saturday?

b) What is the cost of five journeys to London, one on each weekday?

a) (Look along the line for Alton Towers until you get to the column for Saturday.)

The cost is £4.50.

b) Cost for Monday to Thursday = 4 × £4.60

$$= £18.40$$

Cost for Friday = £5.50

Total cost = £23.90

1. Use the information in the worked example opposite to find the cost of the following sets of journeys.

   a) Four journeys to Birmingham on Sunday.

   b) Two to London on Saturday and two to Alton Towers on Tuesday.

   c) One on each day of the week (including the weekend) to Birmingham.

   d) I paid £9.30 for two journeys. What might be the two destinations?

2. The table below shows the yearly premiums for insuring house contents in different areas.
   The size of the premium depends on the type of area (for example whether there are many burglaries in the area or whether there is a likelihood of flooding) and also on the value of the contents.

   House contents insurance premiums

Sum insured	Area 1	Area 2	Area 3
£4000	£46	£40	£35
£5000	£57	£49	£44
£6000	£68	£59	£52
£7000	£79	£68	£61
£8000	£90	£78	£70

   Give the premium for insuring house contents

   a) of value £5000 in Area 2   b) of value £7000 in Area 3

   c) Mr Jones' premium is £52. What is the value of his house contents? What area is the house in?

   d) The Feathers live in Area 3 and their house contents are valued at £5000. The difference between the Feathers' insurance and that of the Drews is £15.
   What is the value of the Drews' house contents and which area do they live in?

   e) The Martins and the Barkers live in Area 1. Their combined premiums come to £147. The Martins pay more than the Barkers.
   What sums do they each insure?

3. In a mail order catalogue the following table gives information about the measurements, in centimetres, of the children the clothes are designed for.

Size	Height	To fit chest	To fit waist	Outside leg	Skirt length
A	86	51	51	48	23
B	92	53	51	53	23
C	98	53	53	56	28
D	104	56	53	58	28
E	110	58	56	63	33

a) Jane's height is 98 cm and she has a waist measurement of 51 cm. If she orders a size C, what will the difference in waist size be?

b) The length of a skirt is 33 cm. What size garment is this?

c) Jim's chest measurement is 56 cm. According to the table, what is the outside leg measurement to go with this chest size?

d) Susan's height is 86 cm and her chest measurement is 53 cm. Which size should be chosen for her school blouse? Why have you chosen this size?

e) John's height is 101 cm, his chest measurement is 53 cm and his outside leg measurement is 57 cm. Which size should be chosen and why?

USING NETWORKS

Information can be presented using a diagram of a special sort called a network.

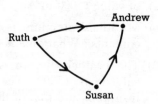

To get information from the diagram you need to know what the line with the arrow means.

In this case it means "is older than", so if you start at the name Ruth and follow the line to Andrew you will read it as "Ruth is older than Andrew".

We can also see that Ruth is older than Susan and Susan is older than Andrew, so it follows that Ruth is the oldest, Andrew is the youngest and Susan is in the middle.

EXERCISE 21c

In this network, the line with the arrow means "is a multiple of".

a) Is 6 a multiple of 3?
b) Is 9 a multiple of 2?

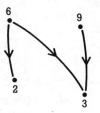

a) 6 is a multiple of 3 (there is an arrow from 6 to 3)

b) 9 is not a multiple of 2 (there is no arrow from 9 to 2)

1. In this network, the line with the arrow means "is a parent of".

a) Who is Anne's parent?
b) Is Gary the parent of Dawn?
c) What relation is Dawn to Anne?
d) What relation is David to Gary?
e) What relation is Anne to Gary?

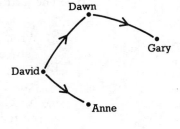

2. The line with the arrow means "is older than".

a) Who is the oldest of the four?
b) Is Ian older or younger than Angela?
c) Is James younger than Ian?

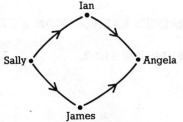

d) Suppose we are now told that Ian is older than James. Copy the diagram and add a line with an arrow to show this.

e) Is Sally older than Angela? If she is, add a line with an arrow to the diagram to show this.

3. This network shows the relationship "is a factor of". (There is a bridge on the line joining 2 to 4 to avoid the line from 3 to 12.)

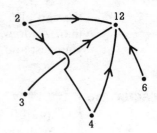

a) According to this diagram, what are the factors of 12?

b) Does 4 have a factor?

c) There are two lines missing. Copy the diagram and add the missing lines.

4. This time the arrow means "is a brother of".

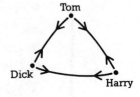

a) What is the difference between this and the other networks? Why does this one have to be marked in a different way?

b) Do all three belong to the same family?

5. The arrow means "is a cousin of".

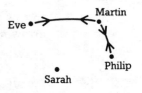

a) Write down the relationship between Philip and Martin.

b) What do you know about Sarah?

c) Angela is Sarah's cousin but no relation of the other three. Copy and complete the diagram.

MIXED EXERCISE ON NETWORKS

EXERCISE 21d 1.

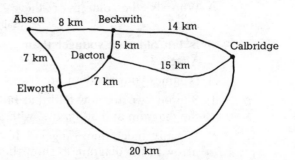

The road map on p. 276 shows the distances between towns.

a) How far is it from Beckwith to Elworth?

b) One possible route from Abson to Calbridge is via Beckwith and Dacton.
List as many other routes as you can from Abson to Calbridge and give the length of each.

c) Is it possible to visit all five towns without going to any of them twice?

d) Is it possible to draw the network without lifting pen from paper?

2. If possible, draw the following diagrams without lifting pen from paper.

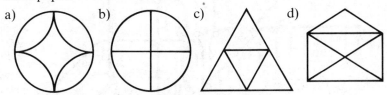

a)   b)   c)   d)

3.

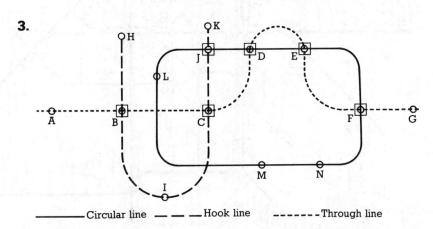

————— Circular line — — — Hook line - - - - - - -Through line

This diagram shows a rail network made up of three systems. It is possible to change from one system to another at the stations marked ▣.

We can describe a route from I to E as
    Hook Line from I to J, then Circular Line clockwise from J to E

a) Describe a good route from A to L.

b) Describe a good route from I to G.

c) Describe four different sensible routes from N to B.
    Which do you think is probably the best and why?

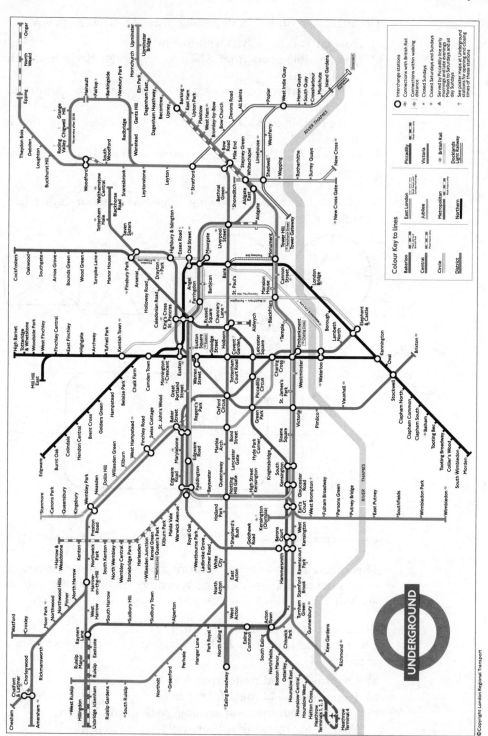

4. Draw this diagram without lifting pen from paper and without going over any line twice.

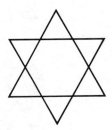

5.

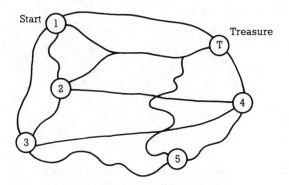

This map shows where clues are hidden for a treasure hunt.

a) Is it possible to collect all the clues in order without going back to any of the hiding places a second time?

b) The path from clue 3 to clue 4 is flooded, though it is still possible to get from clue 5 to the treasure. Is it possible to get round the course now without going back to any of the hiding places a second time?

6. Use the London Underground map opposite to answer the following questions. Describe a possible route from

a) Russell Square (Piccadilly Line) to Westbourne Park (Metropolitan Line),

b) Sloane Square (District and Circle Lines) to Charing Cross (Jubilee and Northern Lines),

c) Borough (Northern Line) to Maida Vale (Bakerloo Line),

d) Kew Gardens (District Line) to Swiss Cottage (Jubilee Line).

e) What is the smallest number of changes you would need to make in travelling from Turnpike Lane (Piccadilly Line) to Clapham South (Northern Line)?

f) Does it look like a good idea to try travelling on the Underground from Edgeware (Northern Line) to Stanmore (Jubilee Line)?

Give a reason for your answer.

7.

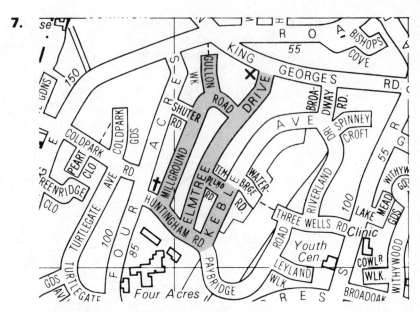

Reproduced by permission of Geographer's A–Z Map Co. Ltd. Based upon the Ordnance Survey map with the permission of the Controller of Her Majesty's Stationery Office, © Crown Copyright.

A copymaster of this map is available in the Answer Book.
John delivers a weekly newspaper to all the houses in the roads shaded grey on this map. In each road, there are houses on both sides.

a) Trace just the shaded roads.
b) John starts his delivery round at the point marked with a cross on this map. He delivers to houses on both sides as he goes down a road. Is it possible to deliver to all the roads without having to go down a road for a second time?
   (He does not have to return to his starting point.)
c) Show a possible route that John could take so that he walks as short a distance as possible. Mark the line with arrows to show the direction.

John decides to avoid crossing backwards and forwards across a road by delivering to houses on one side separately from delivering to houses on the other side.

d) Make another tracing of the map.
e) Is it possible for him to complete the paper round without having to walk past some houses a second time? It does not matter where he finishes the delivery.
f) Show a good route for John's new round.

22 PYTHAGORAS' THEOREM

SQUARES

We obtain the square of a number when we multiply the number by itself,

e.g. the square of 5 is 5×5 which is 25

We write $5^2 = 25$

Similarly $13^2 = 169$ and $2.4^2 = 5.76$

EXERCISE 22a Without using a calculator, write down the squares of the following numbers.

1. 4	**5.** 3	**9.** 6
2. 8	**6.** 7	**10.** 10
3. 12	**7.** 9	**11.** 20
4. 30	**8.** 40	**12.** 70

Use a calculator to find 0.07^2

$0.07^2 = 0.0049$ ($\boxed{0}$ $\boxed{\cdot}$ $\boxed{0}$ $\boxed{7}$ $\boxed{x^2}$ $\boxed{=}$)

Use a calculator to find the squares of the following numbers. Give exact answers.

13. 0.3	**17.** 0.4	**21.** 0.6
14. 1.1	**18.** 1.2	**22.** 0.2
15. 0.7	**19.** 0.5	**23.** 0.07
16. 0.02	**20.** 0.06	**24.** 0.004

> Use a calculator to find the square of 64.8
> Give your answer correct to 4 s.f.
>
> $$64.8^2 = 4199 \vert 0$$
> $$= 4199 \text{ correct to 4 s.f.}$$

Use a calculator to find the squares of the following numbers. Give your answers correct to 4 s.f.

25.	8.7	**29.**	7.3	**33.**	9.4
26.	4.3	**30.**	5.6	**34.**	6.5
27.	12.2	**31.**	24.5	**35.**	17.9
28.	33.6	**32.**	47.8	**36.**	23.7
37.	1.732	**41.**	1.414	**45.**	2.236
38.	37.32	**42.**	29.71	**46.**	56.24
39.	8.734	**43.**	6.554	**47.**	3.928
40.	69.45	**44.**	78.22	**48.**	83.17

SQUARE ROOTS

The square root of a number is the number which when multiplied by itself, gives the original number,

e.g. since $5^2 = 25$, the square root of 25 is 5.

The square root could also be -5, since $(-5) \times (-5) = 25$ but here we are concerned only with positive square roots.

We write $\sqrt{25} = 5$

EXERCISE 22b Without using a calculator, write down the square root of each of the following numbers.

1.	16	**5.**	4	**9.**	36
2.	81	**6.**	64	**10.**	49
3.	1	**7.**	100	**11.**	144
4.	9	**8.**	121	**12.**	25

> Use a calculator to find, correct to 4 s.f., the square root
> of 39.2; check your answer by squaring it.
>
> $$\sqrt{39.2} = 6.260|9 \quad (\boxed{3}\ \boxed{9}\ \boxed{\cdot}\ \boxed{2}\ \boxed{\sqrt{}}\ \boxed{=})$$
>
> $$= 6.261 \text{ to 4 s.f.}$$
>
> Check: $6.261^2 = 39.18\ldots$

Use a calculator to find, correct to 4 s.f., the square roots of the
following numbers. Check your answers by squaring them.

13. 84	**16.** 19	**19.** 29
14. 147	**17.** 39	**20.** 138
15. 727	**18.** 432	**21.** 76

22. 62.3	**25.** 54.29	**28.** 5.443
23. 519.7	**26.** 42.7	**29.** 73.16
24. 3.926	**27.** 224.8	**30.** 73.8

EXERCISE 22c Use a calculator to find the following squares or square roots. Give
your answers correct to 4 s.f. where necessary. Check your answers
using the reverse process.

1. 5.47^2	**5.** 3.64^2	**9.** 1.993^2
2. $\sqrt{34.2}$	**6.** $\sqrt{84.3}$	**10.** $\sqrt{50.2}$
3. 75.3^2	**7.** 12.6^2	**11.** 57.7^2
4. $\sqrt{240}$	**8.** $\sqrt{500}$	**12.** $\sqrt{747}$

13. $\sqrt{1.747}$	**17.** $\sqrt{9.345}$	**21.** $\sqrt{29.21}$
14. 1.747^2	**18.** 9.345^2	**22.** 29.21^2
15. 79.24^2	**19.** 18.91^2	**23.** 57.67^2
16. $\sqrt{349.2}$	**20.** $\sqrt{763.8}$	**24.** $\sqrt{693.4}$

RIGHT-ANGLED TRIANGLES

Equilateral triangles and isosceles triangles are special triangles because they have special properties.

Right-angled triangles are another group of special triangles.

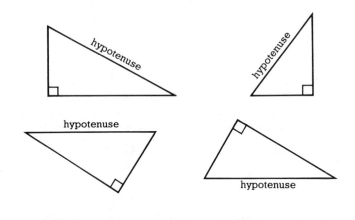

A right-angled triangle has one angle which is 90°.

The side opposite the right-angle is called the *hypotenuse*.

EXERCISE 22d In each of these triangles name the angle that is the right-angle and name the side that is the hypotenuse. The first one is done for you.

1.

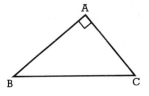

$\widehat{A} = 90°$
BC is the hypotenuse.

3.

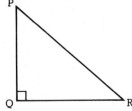

2.

4.

5.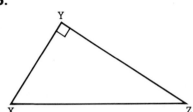

6.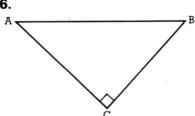

INVESTIGATING RELATIONSHIPS

We are now going to look at the relationship between the lengths of the sides in a right-angled triangle.

EXERCISE 22e Draw each of these triangles full size on 1 cm squared paper. In each case measure and write down the length of the hypotenuse. Draw and measure carefully otherwise you will not get any useful evidence from your drawings.

1.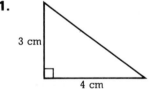

4.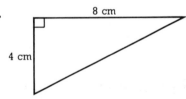

2.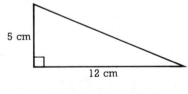

5.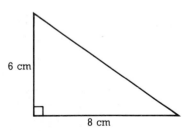

3.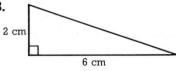

6.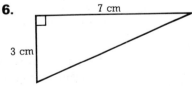

7.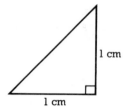

8.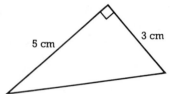

9. In each question from 1 to 8, find the squares of the lengths of the three sides. If necessary give the squares correct to the nearest square centimetre. Copy this table and fill in your answers.

	1	2	3	4	5	6	7	8
Length of shortest side squared								
Length of middle side squared								
Length of longest side squared								

Can you see a relation between the first two values and the third value?

PYTHAGORAS' THEOREM

If your drawing and measuring is reasonably accurate, you will find that the sum of the squares of the lengths of the shortest and middle sides is equal to the square of the length of the longest side.

This result is known as *Pythagoras' Theorem* and it states that

> in any right-angled triangle,
> the square of the length of the hypotenuse is equal to
> the sum of the squares of the lengths of the other two sides

If we know the length of two sides of a right-angled triangle, we can now use Pythagoras' Theorem to find the length of the third side.

We start with some practice in writing out Pythagoras' Theorem for different triangles.

EXERCISE 22f

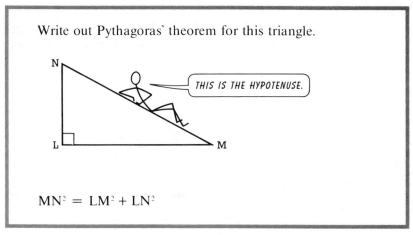

Write out Pythagoras' theorem for this triangle.

THIS IS THE HYPOTENUSE.

$MN^2 = LM^2 + LN^2$

Write out Pythagoras' Theorem for each triangle.

1.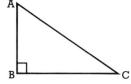

4.

2.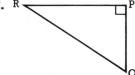

5.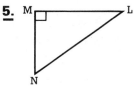

3.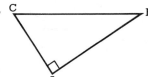

6.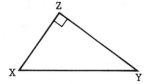

FINDING THE LENGTH OF THE HYPOTENUSE

We start by writing out Pythagoras' Theorem. This gives a formula and we can put the numbers in their correct places.

EXERCISE 22g

Find the length of the hypotenuse of this triangle. Give your answer correct to three significant figures.

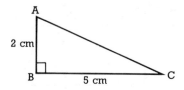

AC is the hypotenuse so   (Pythagoras' Theorem)

$$AC^2 = AB^2 + BC^2$$
$$AC^2 = 2^2 + 5^2$$
$$= 4 + 25$$
$$= 29$$
$$\therefore \qquad AC = \sqrt{29}$$
$$= 5.38\vert5$$

The length of the hypotenuse is 5.39 cm correct to 3 s.f.

Find the length of the hypotenuse of each triangle. Where necessary give your answers correct to three significant figures.

1.

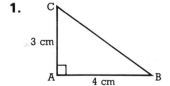

3.

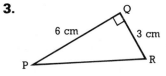

2.

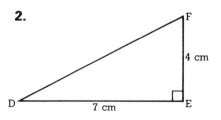

4.

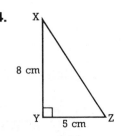

Find the length of the hypotenuse of this triangle. Give your answer correct to three significant figures.

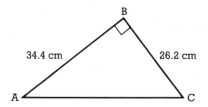

AC is the hypotenuse, so

$$AC^2 = AB^2 + BC^2 \quad (\text{Pythagoras' theorem})$$

$$AC^2 = 34 \cdot 4^2 + 26 \cdot 2^2$$

(Write down the first *four* significant figures from the display at each step (↑), but do *not* clear the display between steps.)

$$= 1183 \cdot \ldots + 686 \cdot 4 \ldots$$

$$= 1869 \cdot \ldots$$

$$\therefore AC = \sqrt{1869 \cdot \ldots} \quad (\boxed{\sqrt{}}\ \boxed{=})$$

IF YOU DO ACCIDENTALLY CLEAR YOUR CALCULATOR, KEY IN 1869 BEFORE PRESSING $\boxed{\sqrt{}}$.

$$= 43 \cdot 2 \vert 4$$

The length of the hypotenuse is 43.2 cm correct to 3 s.f.

Find the length of the hypotenuse of each triangle. Give your answers correct to three significant figures.

5.

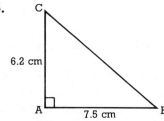

6.

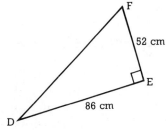

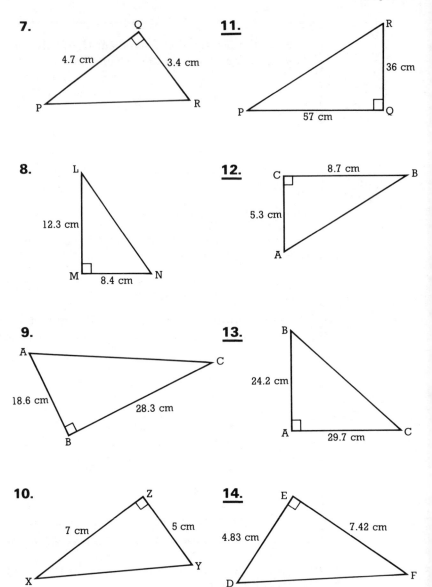

7.
Q

4.7 cm   3.4 cm

P   R

11.
R

36 cm

P   Q
57 cm

8.
L

12.3 cm

M   N
8.4 cm

12.
C   8.7 cm   B

5.3 cm

A

9.
A   C

18.6 cm   28.3 cm

B

13.
B

24.2 cm

A   C
29.7 cm

10.
Z

7 cm   5 cm

X   Y

14.
E

4.83 cm   7.42 cm

D   F

FINDING ONE OF THE SHORTER SIDES

If we are given the length of the hypotenuse and one other side, we can find the length of the third side. We do this by writing out the formula for Pythagoras' Theorem and then putting the numbers in their correct positions. This gives an equation which we can solve.

EXERCISE 22h

Find the length of BC. Give your answer correct to three significant figures.

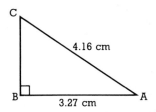

$$AC^2 = AB^2 + BC^2 \qquad \text{(Pythagoras' Theorem)}$$

$$4.16^2 = 3.27^2 + BC^2$$

Take 3.27^2 from each side $\qquad 4.16^2 - 3.27^2 = BC^2$

(Remember to write down the first four significant figures at each stage.)

$$17.30\ldots - 10.69\ldots = BC^2$$

$$6.612\ldots = BC^2$$

$$BC = \sqrt{6.612}\ldots$$

$$= 2.57\,|\,1$$

The length of BC is 2.57 cm correct to 3 s.f.

Find the length of the unmarked side in each triangle. Give your answers correct to three significant figures.

1.   **2.**

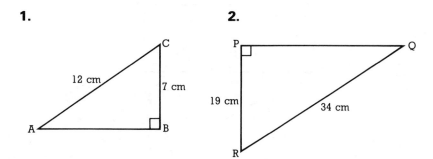

3.

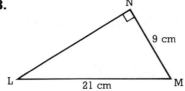

4.

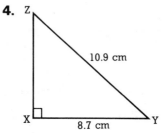

5.

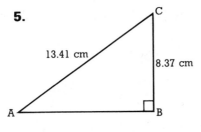

6.

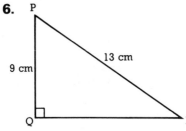

7.

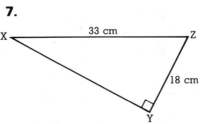

8.

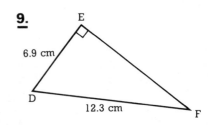

9.

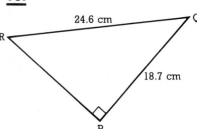

10.

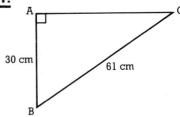

11.

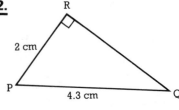

12.

GRAPHICAL USE OF PYTHAGORAS' THEOREM TO FIND THE SQUARE ROOTS OF THE NATURAL NUMBERS

EXERCISE 22i **1.** Construct a right-angled triangle and find the hypotenuse when the other two sides are of unit length (1 inch is a good unit to use).

2. Continue your construction from question 1 using each hypotenuse, together with a side of 1 unit, as the sides forming the right angle for the next triangle. You will find that the answers get more inaccurate as you go up but $\sqrt{4} = 2$ will act as a check on the accuracy of your work.

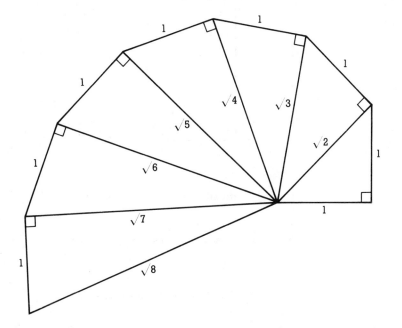

Use this method to find the square root of each whole number up to 8.

3. Compare these results with the values obtained from your calculator. If your values are accurate you might like to continue further.

PROBLEMS

When using a calculator, write your intermediate calculations to four significant figures. In the next exercise give all your answers correct to three significant figures.

EXERCISE 22j

A wire stay supporting a telegraph pole is 10 m long. It is attached to a point 1 m from the top of the pole and to a point 4 m from the base of the pole on level ground. Find the height of the telegraph pole.

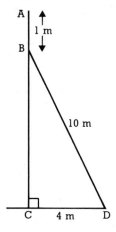

Let ABC represent the vertical pole and BD the wire stay.

In triangle BCD Pythagoras' result gives

$$BD^2 = BC^2 + CD^2$$

i.e.
$$10^2 = BC^2 + 4^2$$

$$100 = BC^2 + 16$$

$$84 = BC^2$$

$$BC = \sqrt{84}$$

∴
$$BC = 9.165$$

Height of pole is 9.165 m + 1 m = 10.165 m

= 10.2 m correct to 3 s.f.

Remember to draw a diagram for each question.

1. A football pitch measures 120 yd by 80 yd. How far is it between opposite corners?

2. A hockey pitch measures 60 m by 95 m. Find the length of a diagonal on the pitch.

3. A rugby pitch measures 100 m by 70 m. How far is it between opposite corners?

4. A tennis court measures 29.6 m by 10.7 m. How far is it between opposite corners? Give your answer correct to the nearest tenth of a metre.

5. One diagonal of a front door, which is 0.813 m wide, is 2.03 m. How high is the door?

6. The diagonal of a rectangular sheet of glass is 73 cm. If the rectangle is 58 cm long, how wide is it?

Questions 7 to 12 refer to the chess board given below.

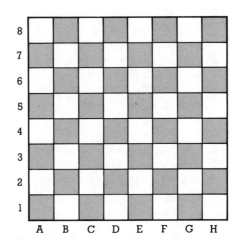

Assume that the side of each square is 4 cm.

How far is it from

7. the bottom left corner of A1 to the top right corner of H8?

8. the bottom left corner of A1 to the top right corner of G4?

9. the bottom left corner of C3 to the top right corner of F8?

10. the top left corner of B2 to the bottom right corner of E7?

11. the top right corner of B3 to the bottom right corner of H6?

12. the top right corner of D2 to the top left corner of G5?

13. A wire stay, 12 m long, is attached to a flag pole 2 m from the top. The other end of the wire is fixed to a point in level ground 9 m from the base of the pole. How high is the pole?

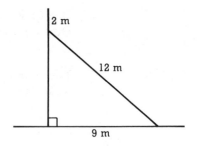

14. A ship sails 27 nautical miles due south, then 20 nautical miles due east. How far is it from its starting point?

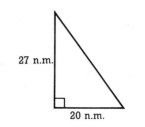

15. A rectangular classroom measures 7.5 m by 5.5 m. What is the length of the longest straight line that can be drawn on the floor?

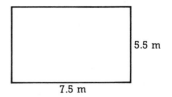

16. This diagram shows a section of the ridged roof of a farm building. The section is 8 m wide and 1.5 m high. If the building is 12 m long find

a) the length of the sloping side, BC, in metres
b) the total area of the sloping roof in square metres.

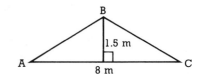

17. The rear doors of a van each measure 2 m by 0.75 m. Find the width of the largest board of negligible thickness that can be loaded into the van.

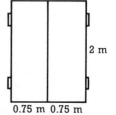

MIXED EXERCISE

EXERCISE 22k

1. Use a calculator to find, correct to 3 s.f.,

a) 0.874^2 b) 5.93^2

2. Use a calculator to find, correct to 3 s.f.,

a) $\sqrt{0.0874}$ b) $\sqrt{593}$

3. Use the information given in the diagram to find the length of QR.

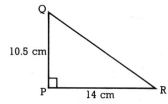

4. Use the information given in the diagram to find the length of BC.

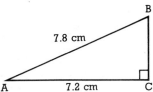

5. Calculate, correct to 3 s.f., the length of the diagonal of a square of side 15 cm.

6. Use the information given in the diagram to find

a) BC   b) AC   c) AD

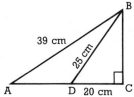

7. The diagonals of a rhombus have lengths 12 cm and 16 cm. Find the length of a side.

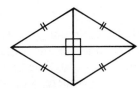

23 FLOW DIAGRAMS

MAKING FLOW DIAGRAMS

Charlotte wants to use an electric kettle to boil some water. The various things she has to do are: plug it in, wait until it turns itself off, fill it with water, take the lid off, put the lid on, switch the power on.

While these events are not listed above in a correct order, and while several different orders are possible, a safe, satisfactory order would be

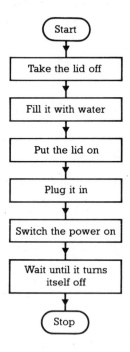

This is an example of a flow diagram. Flow diagrams are useful when deciding on the order of the steps needed in doing a job. Sometimes it is possible to carry out the steps in different orders. On other occasions there is only one correct order.

We can show this with simple arithmetic.

$$8 + 4 = 12$$

and $$4 + 8 = 12$$

i.e. for addition changing the order of the numbers does not alter the result

but $$8 \div 4 = 2$$

and $$4 \div 8 = 0.5$$

i.e. for division changing the order of the numbers gives a different answer.

EXERCISE 23a

> Arrange the numbers and symbols   4   5   9 $-$ $=$ in order to make a correct statement.
>
>
>
> $$9 - 5 = 4$$

1. Arrange the numbers and symbols in order to make a correct statement
   a) 12   7   5   +   =
   b) 3   4   12   ÷   =
   c) 2   3   4   2   × $-$ =
   d) 3   3   4   13   +   ×   =

2. Arrange each of these sets of statements in order, using a flow diagram.

   Each one should begin with (Start) and end with (Stop)

   a)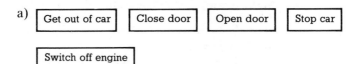

   b)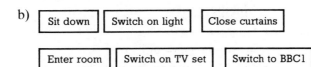

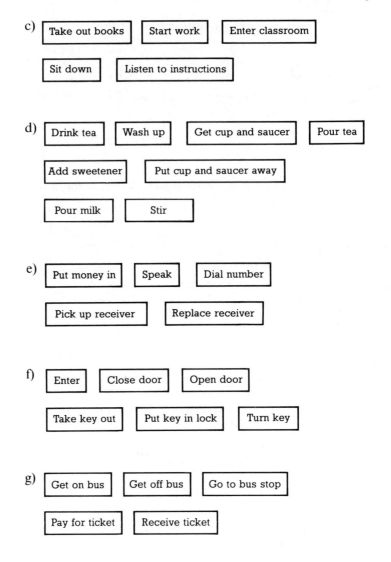

c)

| Take out books | Start work | Enter classroom |

| Sit down | Listen to instructions |

d)

| Drink tea | Wash up | Get cup and saucer | Pour tea |

| Add sweetener | Put cup and saucer away |

| Pour milk | Stir |

e)

| Put money in | Speak | Dial number |

| Pick up receiver | Replace receiver |

f)

| Enter | Close door | Open door |

| Take key out | Put key in lock | Turn key |

g)

| Get on bus | Get off bus | Go to bus stop |

| Pay for ticket | Receive ticket |

3. Make a simple flow diagram for each of these actions.

a) Getting up
b) Going to bed
c) Washing your hair
d) Making a cake
e) Changing a wheel after having a puncture
f) Warming a can of beans
g) Playing a tape or compact disc.

FUNCTION MACHINES

In Book 1B we looked at function machines. A function machine is a simple example of a flow chart. Function machines were drawn across the page whereas the flow diagram on page 298 is drawn down the page. Both directions are acceptable. The direction depends on the amount of information in the flow chart.

EXERCISE 23b

Construct a flow chart to give the value of $4x + 7$ for a given value of x. Use it to find the value of $4x + 7$ when

a) $x = 5$ b) $x = \frac{1}{2}$

a) If $x = 5$ $5 \longrightarrow 20 \longrightarrow 27$

b) If $x = \frac{1}{2}$ $\frac{1}{2} \longrightarrow 2 \longrightarrow 9$

Construct a flow diagram for finding

1. the value of $5x - 3$ for a given value of x. Use it to find the value of $5x - 3$ when   a) $x = 5$ b) $x = 12$

2. the value of $8x + 1$ for a given value of x. Use it to find the value of $8x + 1$ when   a) $x = 1$ b) $x = 5$

3. the value of $9 - x$ for a given value of x. Use it to find the value of $9 - x$ when   a) $x = 6$ b) $x = 9$

4. the value of $12 - 3x$ for a given value of x. Use it to find the value of $12 - 3x$ when   a) $x = 2$ b) $x = 3$

5. the value of $x^2 + 4$ for a given value of x. Use it to find the value of $x^2 + 4$ when   a) $x = 5$ b) $x = 0$

6. the value of $3x^2$ for a given value of x. Use it to find the value of $3x^2$ when   a) $x = 2$ b) $x = 5$

DECISION BOXES

In Book 2B we looked at decision trees. A *decision box* is diamond shaped and contains a question that can be answered either "Yes" or "No". Some flow charts include decision boxes and an example is given below. This flow chart shows the steps included in deciding what to do in the morning.

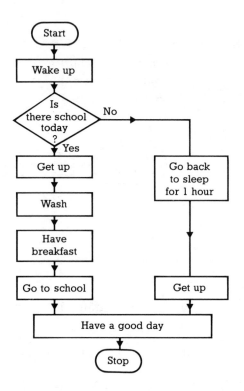

EXERCISE 23c 1. Liz wants a hot drink. You can offer her tea or coffee. Use the boxes given below to make a suitable flow chart.

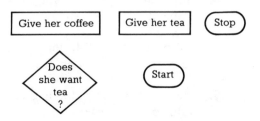

2. Julie is thirsty and wishes to have a drink. John has squash, cola and lemonade. Make a suitable flow chart for John using the following boxes.

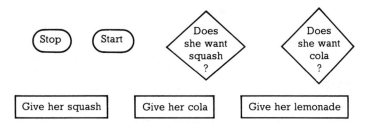

3. Peter would like some fruit. You have apples, oranges and bananas. Make a suitable flow chart from the following boxes.

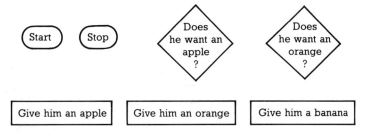

4. Make a flow chart from the following boxes to find whether or not a given number is divisible by 12, by finding whether or not it is divisible by 3 and by 4.

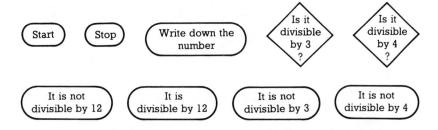

5. Make your own flow chart to find whether or not a given number is divisible by 24.

6. The size of each of the three angles of a triangle is known. Draw a flow chart to test whether or not the triangle is equilateral.

LOOPS

An instruction like "Wait until it is safe to cross the road" causes problems since it is really a mixture of questions and instructions. If the answer to a decision box is "No" the whole process must be repeated. Rather than write it out again we use a loop. This takes us back to the beginning and we can keep going round the loop until we are ready to move on.

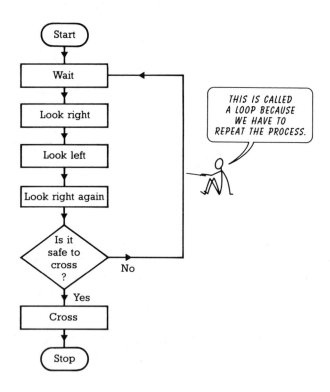

Sometimes we can use decision boxes to try to solve mathematical problems.

EXERCISE 23d Here is a flow chart for finding the first four terms of a sequence.

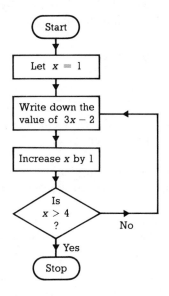

Use the flow chart to write down the first four terms of the sequence.

Start $\rightarrow x = 1 \rightarrow 3x - 2 = 1 \rightarrow$ increase x by 1
$\quad\quad \rightarrow x = 2 \rightarrow 3x - 2 = 4 \rightarrow$ increase x by 1
$\quad\quad \rightarrow x = 3 \rightarrow 3x - 2 = 7 \rightarrow$ increase x by 1
$\quad\quad \rightarrow x = 4 \rightarrow 3x - 2 = 10 \rightarrow$ increase x by 1
$\quad\quad \rightarrow x = 5 \rightarrow$ Stop

The first four terms are 1, 4, 7, 10

1. Referring to the flow chart given above

a) Why is the question ⟨Is $x > 4$?⟩ needed?

b) How many terms of the sequence would you get if you

replaced ⟨Is $x > 4$?⟩ by ⟨Is $x > 6$?⟩ ?

2. a) Draw the flow chart given on the previous page but replace $3x - 2$ by $2x + 5$. Use this flow chart to write down the first four terms of the sequence.

b) What would you replace 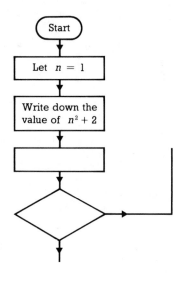 by if you wanted the

first ten terms?

c) Draw the flow chart required to give the first eight terms of the sequence.

3. Copy and complete this flow chart and use it to write down the first six terms of the sequence.

24 COORDINATES AND GRAPHS

COORDINATES

To fix the position of a point in a plane we use two axes, an *x*-axis (drawn across the page) and a *y*-axis (drawn up the page).
The point where these axes cross is called *the origin*.

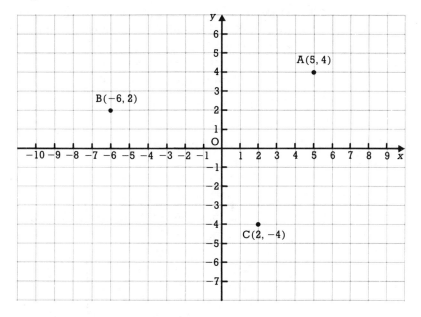

If we start from O and go 5 units to the *right*

and then go 4 units *up*

we get to the point A which we can describe by
the pair of numbers (5, 4).

The numbers 5 and 4 are called *the coordinates* of A,

5 is the *x*-coordinate and 4 is the *y*-coordinate.

When we describe the position of a point by its coordinates, we always put the *x*-coordinate first.

The point B has coordinates (−6, 2). This means that, starting from O, we go 6 units to the *left* and 2 units *up*.

The point C (2, −4) is 2 units to the *right* and 4 units *down*.

EXERCISE 24a **1.** Draw x and y axes on squared paper, numbering each axis from −6 to +6. Plot the points: A(−4, −3), B(3, −3), C(3, 1) and D(−4, 1).

Join A to B, B to C, C to D and D to A.

What is the name of the shape ABCD?

2. Draw x and y axes on squared paper, numbering each axis from −6 to +6. Plot the following points: A(3, −2), B(5, −2), C(0, 4), D(−5, −2), E(−3, −2), F(−1, 0) and G(1, 0).

Join the points in alphabetical order and join G to A.

3. Draw x and y axes on squared paper, numbering each one from −6 to 6. Plot the following points: A(4, 3), B(2, 5), C(−2, 5), D(−4, 3), E(−4, −3), F(−2, −3), G(−2, −1), H(2, −1), I(2, −3), J(4, −3).

Join the points in order and join J to A.

LINES PARALLEL TO THE AXES

A vertical line is parallel to the y-axis and a horizontal line is parallel to the x-axis.

Consider the set of points that each have an x coordinate of 2.

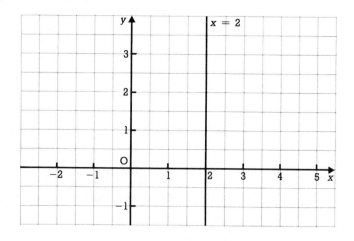

We can write x-coordinate = 2

or simply $x = 2$

This is called the *equation of the line*.

Now consider the equation $y = 4$.

This means the set of points that each have a y-coordinate of 4.

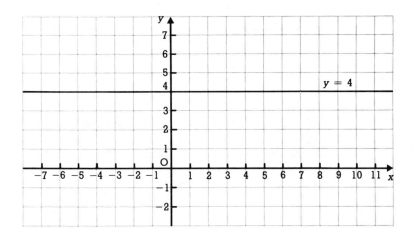

Therefore $y = 4$ represents a horizontal line which is 4 units above the origin.

EXERCISE 24b Write down the equation of each line.

1.

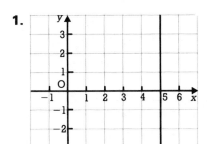

3.

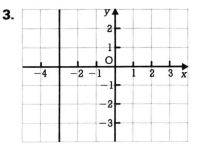

2.

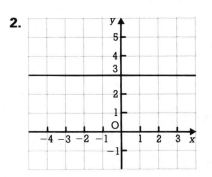

4.

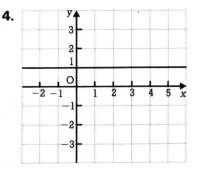

5. 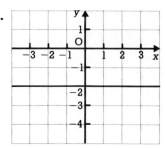   **6.**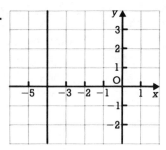

Use squared paper to draw the line with the given equation.

7. $x = 3$ **9.** $x = 2$ **11.** $x = -2$

8. $y = 4$ **10.** $y = 7$ **12.** $y = -4$

SLANT LINES THROUGH THE ORIGIN

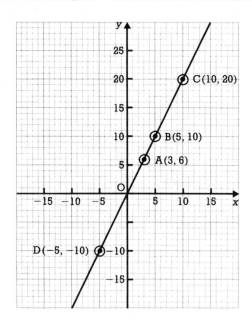

A, B, C and D are some of the points on the line in the diagram.

For each of these points

$$y\text{-coordinate} = 2 \times x\text{-coordinate.}$$

Therefore the equation of the line is $y = 2x$

EXERCISE 24c

Draw x and y axes, numbering each one from -20 to $+20$ at 5-unit intervals using 1 cm for 5 units on each axis.

a) Plot the points A(10, -5), B(16, -8), C(-10, 5).

b) Draw the straight line through A, B and C.

c) On your line, mark the point D whose x-coordinate is 20. What is the y-coordinate of D?

d) Find the connection between the x and y coordinates of each of the points A, B, C and D.

e) Write down the equation of this line.

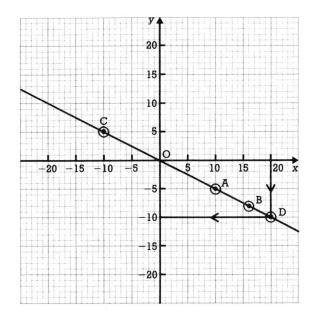

c) From the guide lines on the graph, the y-coordinate of D is -10.

d) The y-coordinate is half the size of the x-coordinate, but has the opposite sign,
i.e. the y-coordinate $= -\frac{1}{2} \times$ the x-coordinate.

e) $y = -\frac{1}{2}x$

Use graph paper for questions 1 to 3.

Draw x and y axes, numbering each one from -20 to $+20$ at 5-unit intervals using 1 cm for 5 units on each axis.

1. a) Plot the points A(5, 5), B(18, 18), C(−10, −10).

   b) Draw the straight line through A, B and C.

   c) On your line mark the point D whose x-coordinate is 10. What is the y-coordinate of D?

   d) What is the connection between the x and y coordinates for each of the points A, B, C and D?

   e) Write down the equation of this line.

2. a) Plot the points A(1, 3), B(5, 15), C(−4, −12).

   b) Draw the straight line through A, B and C.

   c) On your line, mark the point D whose x-coordinate is 2. What is the y-coordinate of D?

   d) What is the connection between the x and y coordinates of each of the points A, B, C and D?

   e) Write down the equation of this line.

3. a) Plot the points A(10, 5), B(20, 10), C(−5, −2.5).

   b) Draw the straight line through A, B and C.

   c) On your line, mark the point D whose x-coordinate is 5. What is the y-coordinate of D?

   d) What is the connection between the x and y coordinates for each of the points A, B, C and D?

   e) Write down the equation of this line.

DIRECTED NUMBERS

We use numbers to describe quantities. For example we may talk about $\frac{2}{3}$ of a cake, 10.5 cm of wire, 35 apples, and so on.

These numbers, $\frac{2}{3}$, 10.5 and 35, are examples of *positive numbers*.

We cannot however use positive numbers to describe temperatures below 0°C (the freezing point of water), or any other quantity that can fall below a zero level.

To do this we need *negative numbers*.

Positive numbers are written, for example, as +2 or simply as 2. Negative numbers are written, for example, as −2.

Positive numbers and negative numbers are together known as *directed numbers*.

USING DIRECTED NUMBERS

Consider the line whose equation is $y = 1 - 2x$

If we want to find the y coordinate when $x = -3$, then we need to work out $1 - 2 \times (-3)$

There are rules for multiplying and dividing directed numbers which are based on common sense.

For example, suppose that we want to melt an ice-cube; we do this by warming it up, i.e. to remove the frozen state of the water, we add warmth.

In mathematical language we would say "to take away a negative number, we add a positive one."

e.g. $$4 - (-2) = 4 + 2$$

Now $\qquad -2 \times (-3)$ means take away 2 lots of -3,

i.e. $\qquad -2 \times (-3) = -(-6) = +6$

USING A CALCULATOR

We can use a calculator to work with a mixture of positive and negative numbers. To enter a negative number we can use the $\boxed{+/_-}$ button. This button changes the sign of a number, e.g. to enter -6, press $\boxed{6}$ $\boxed{+/_-}$

(On some calculators it is possible to enter, say, -6 directly by pressing $\boxed{-}$ $\boxed{6}$)

To calculate $-8 \times (-0.7)$ we can press the following sequence of buttons: $\boxed{8}$ $\boxed{+/_-}$ $\boxed{\times}$ $\boxed{0}$ $\boxed{\cdot}$ $\boxed{7}$ $\boxed{+/_-}$ $\boxed{=}$

The next exercise gives practise in using a calculator and we will use the results to deduce the general rules for multiplying and dividing directed numbers.

EXERCISE 24d Use your calculator to find

1. $1.3 \times (-4)$ **3.** $5 \times (-1.7)$ **5.** $1.2 \times (-3)$

2. $(-1.6) \times 7$ **4.** $(-8) \times 2.5$ **6.** $(-5) \times 0.5$

7. In questions 1 to 6, a positive number and a negative number are multiplied together. Look at the signs of the answers and then copy and complete the following sentence.
When a positive number and a negative number are multiplied, the answer is a .... number.

Use your calculator to find

8. $3.6 \div (-2)$ **10.** $12 \div (-0.3)$ **12.** $4 \div (-0.2)$

9. $(-1.2) \div 4$ **11.** $(-24) \div 1.2$ **13.** $(-1.6) \div 8$

14. Look at the signs of your answers to questions 8 to 13 then copy and complete the following sentence.
When dividing numbers with different signs, the answer is a .... number.

Use your calculator to find

15. $(-12) \times (-0.5)$ **17.** $(-1.4) \times (-7)$ **19.** $(-2) \times (-2)$

16. $(-12) \div (-0.5)$ **18.** $(-1.4) \div (-7)$ **20.** $(-1) \times (-2.5)$

21. Use your answers to questions 15 to 20 to complete the following sentence.
When two negative numbers are multiplied or divided, the answer is a .... number.

RULES FOR MULTIPLYING AND DIVIDING DIRECTED NUMBERS

We know that when we multiply or divide two positive numbers we get a positive answer and this fact can be combined with the conclusion drawn in question 21 above to give this rule

> when two numbers with the *same sign* are multiplied or divided, the answer is *positive*.

The conclusions drawn in questions 7 and 14 above can be combined to give this rule

> when two numbers with *opposite signs* are multiplied or divided, the answer is *negative*.

EXERCISE 24e Do not use a calculator for questions 1 to 36.

Find   a) $(-4)^2$ b) $6 \div (-2)$

a) $(-4)^2 = (-4) \times (-4)$
                            $= +16$

b) $6 \div (-2) = -3.$

Find

1. $(3) \times (-2)$ **5.** $(-2) \times (+4)$ **9.** $(-2)^2$

2. $(-2) \times (-6)$ **6.** 5×6 **10.** $(-5) \times (+3)$

3. 7×8 **7.** $(+3) \times (-4)$ **11.** $(-3)^2$

4. $(-3) \times (-9)$ **8.** $(-2) \times (-7)$ **12.** $(+3) \times (-6)$

13. $(+6) \div (+3)$ **17.** $(-8) \div (+4)$ **21.** $4 \div 2$

14. $(+6) \div (-3)$ **18.** $(+10) \div (-2)$ **22.** $(-12) \div (+4)$

15. $(-6) \div (+3)$ **19.** $(+9) \div (+3)$ **23.** $(-3) \div 3$

16. $(-6) \div (-3)$ **20.** $(-5) \div (-1)$ **24.** $15 \div (-5)$

Find $1 - (-2)$

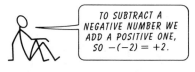

TO SUBTRACT A
NEGATIVE NUMBER WE
ADD A POSITIVE ONE,
SO $-(-2) = +2$.

$1 - (-2) = 1 + 2$
$= 3$

25. $4 - (-3)$ **26.** $-5 + (-3)$ **33.** $7 - 3(-4)$

26. $2 + (-3)$ **30.** $2 - (-4) + 1$ **34.** $-2 + (-5)$

27. $-1 - (-4)$ **31.** $1 - (-2)^2$ **35.** $9 \div (-3)$

28. $2(-2) - (-4)$ **32.** $6 - (4 \div -2)$ **36.** $-4 + (-3)^2$

Use a calculator for the remaining questions in this exercise and give your answers correct to three significant figures. Remember to check that your answer is reasonable, i.e. is it about the right size and is the sign correct?

37. $(-2.5)^2$ **39.** $1.25 \div (-0.66)$ **41.** $1.2 \times (-2.5)^2$

38. $2 \times (-0.25)^2$ **40.** $(-3.66) \div 2.8$ **42.** $(-1.6) \div (-4.5)$

DRAWING A LINE FROM ITS EQUATION

Suppose that we want to draw the line whose equation is $y = 2x$.

For any point on this line,

> the y-coordinate is twice the x-coordinate.

Therefore if we choose a value of x, we can find the corresponding value of y.

We need only two points to draw a straight line, but it is sensible to use a third point as a check.

We will take the points whose x-coordinates are $-3, 0$ and 2.

When $x = -3$, $y = 2 \times (-3) = -6$ so $(-3, -6)$ is on the line.

When $x = 0$, $y = 2 \times (0) = 0$ so $(0, 0)$ is on the line.

When $x = 2$, $y = 2 \times 2 = 4$ so $(2, 4)$ is on the line.

This information is usually listed in a table.

x	-3	0	2
y	-6	0	4

We now plot these points and draw the straight line through them.

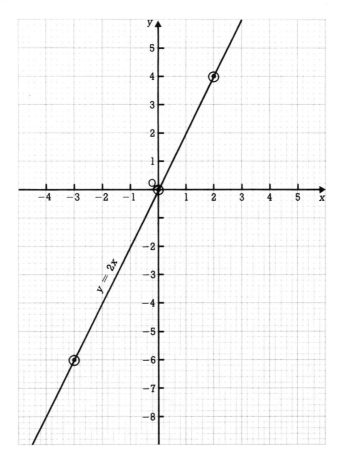

EXERCISE 24f In all the questions in this exercise use graph paper and take 1 cm for 1 unit on both axes.

1. The equation of a line is $y = 4x$. Copy and complete the following table to give the coordinates of three points on the line.

x	-1	0	2
y			

Draw x and y axes for the ranges $-2 \leqslant x \leqslant 3$ and $-8 \leqslant y \leqslant 9$. Plot the three points. If they are in a straight line, draw that line. If they are not in a straight line, check your arithmetic for all three points.

Repeat question 1 for the following equations, drawing x and y axes for the ranges given in brackets.

2. $y = 6x$

x	-1	0	2
y			

$(-2 \leqslant x \leqslant 3, \; -6 \leqslant y \leqslant 12)$

3. $y = \frac{1}{2}x$

x	-6	0	4
y			

$(-6 \leqslant x \leqslant 4, \; -3 \leqslant y \leqslant 2)$

4. $y = -x$

x	0	2	5
y			

$(-2 \leqslant x \leqslant 8, \; -5 \leqslant y \leqslant 3)$

5. $y = -2x$

x	-2	0	4
y			

$(-3 \leqslant x \leqslant 5, \; -8 \leqslant y \leqslant 10)$

6. $y = -4x$

x	-2	0	3
y			

$(-3 \leqslant x \leqslant 4, \; -12 \leqslant y \leqslant 10)$

7. $y = -\frac{1}{2}x$

x	-8	0	6
y			

$(-10 \leqslant x \leqslant 8, \; -4 \leqslant y \leqslant 5)$

8. $y = 3x$

x	-2	0	3
y			

$(-3 \leqslant x \leqslant 4, \; -8 \leqslant y \leqslant 10)$

Not all straight line graphs go through the origin.

EXERCISE 24g

The equation of a straight line is $y = 1 - 2x$. Copy and complete the table to give the coordinates of three points on the line.

x	-2	0	2
y			

Draw x and y axes for the ranges $-3 \leqslant x \leqslant 3$ and $-4 \leqslant y \leqslant 6$ using a scale of 1 cm for 1 unit on each axis. Plot the three points and draw a straight line through them.

When $x = -2$,

$$y = 1 - 2(-2)$$
$$= 1 + 4 = 5$$

When $x = 0$,

$$y = 1 - 2(0)$$
$$= 1 - 0 = 1$$

When $x = 2$,

$$y = 1 - 2(2)$$
$$= 1 - 4 = -3$$

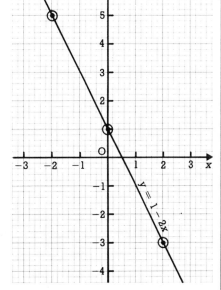

x	-2	0	2
y	5	1	-3

1. The equation of a line is $y = 2x - 3$. Copy and complete the following table to give the coordinates of three points on the line.

x	−1	0	2
y			

Use graph paper and draw the x-axis across the middle and the y-axis up the middle of the sheet. Scale each axis using 1 cm for one 1 unit. Plot the three points and draw a straight line through them. If your points are not in a straight line, check your arithmetic for all three points. Label your line with its equation.

Use the same sheet of graph paper and repeat question 1 for the following lines. Label each line with its equation.

2. $y = x - 2$

x	−1	0	3
y			

3. $y = 2x + 1$

x	−2	0	2
y			

4. $y = 4 - 3x$

x	−1	0	3
y			

5. $y = 3 - x$

x	−2	0	4
y			

You are given the graph of $y = -\frac{1}{4}x$. Use the graph to find   a) y when $x = 6$ b) x when $y = 0.6$

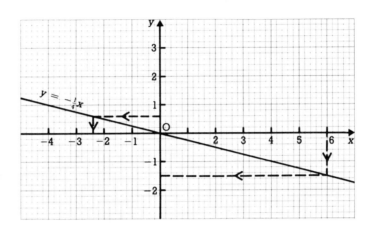

From the guide lines on the graph

a) when $x = 6$, $y = -1.5$

b) when $y = 0.6$, $x = -2.4$

Do not draw on the graphs given for questions 6 to 8. Use a ruler as a guide line if it helps.

6. You are given the graph of $y = \frac{1}{2}x$. Use the graph to find

a) y when $x = 2$ d) x when $y = 2$

b) y when $x = -2$ e) x when $y = 1.2$

c) y when $x = 1.6$ f) x when $y = -0.8$

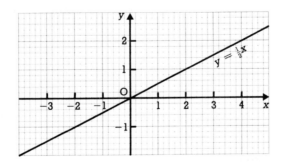

7. You are given the graph of $y = 2x$. Use the graph to find

    a) y when $x = 1$ d) x when $y = 0$

    b) y when $x = -1$ e) x when $y = 1.6$

    c) y when $x = 1.5$ f) x when $y = -2.4$

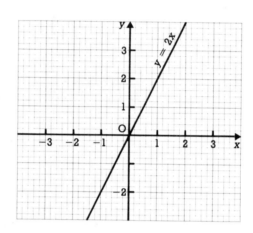

8. You are given the graph of $y = -x$. Use the graph to find

    a) y when $x = 2$ d) x when $y = -3$

    b) y when $x = -1$ e) x when $y = -2.6$

    c) y when $x = 3.4$ f) x when $y = 1.8$

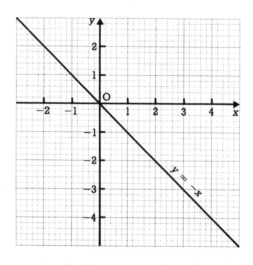

9. This table gives the values of y for some values of x

x	-2	-1	0	1	2	3	4
y	-1	0	1	2	3	4	5

a) Use graph paper and draw x and y axes through the middle of the sheet. Scale the axes using 1 cm for 1 unit on each axis. Plot the points whose coordinates are given in the table. Draw a straight line through them.

b) Look both at the pattern of numbers in the table and at the graph. There is a relationship between the value of x and the corresponding value of y. When you think that you have found it, test it by writing down the value of y when $x = 7$. Check that the graph gives this value for y.

c) Repeat part (b) to find the value of y when $x = 2.5$.

d) What value does y have when $x = 30$?

e) Copy and complete this function machine to show the relationship between values of x and the corresponding values of y.

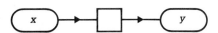

f) Now write down the equation of the line.

10. This table gives the coordinates of points on a straight line.

x	-3	-2	-1	0	1	2	3	4
y	-5	-3	-1	1	3	5	7	9

Use any strategy you like to find the equation of this line. Explain any working that you do.

CURVES

This table gives the coordinates of some points.

x	-3	-2	-1	0	1	2	3
y	9	4	1	0	1	4	9

When these points are plotted, we can see that we can draw a smooth curve through them.

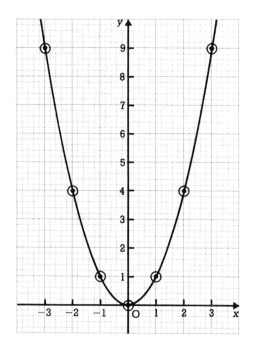

Looking at the numbers in the table, we see that

$$y\text{-coordinate} = (x\text{-coordinate})^2$$

or simply $$y = x^2$$

This is called the equation of the curve.

We can think of the equation of a curve as a formula which, when we put in a value for x, will give a value for y; this gives the coordinates of a point on the curve.

EXERCISE 24h 1. a) Make your own graph of the curve $y = x^2$; start by copying and completing this table. (The extra points will help you to draw a smooth curve.)

x	-3	-2.5	-2	-1.5	-1	-0.5	0	0.5	1	1.5	2	2.5	3
y	9		4	2.25	1	0.25	0		1		4		9

TO USE A CALCULATOR TO FIND THIS VALUE OF y, PRESS 2 · 5 +⁄− × 2 · 5 +⁄− =.

b) Draw x and y axes for the ranges $-4 \leqslant x \leqslant 4$ and $0 \leqslant y \leqslant 10$ using a scale of 2 cm for 1 unit. Plot the points and draw a smooth curve through them.

c) Use your graph to find the value of y when $x = 1.8$. Check your answer by finding the square of 1.8.

2. The equation of a curve is $y = 2x^2$.

a) Copy and complete this table to give the coordinates of some points on the curve.

x	-2	-1	-0.75	-0.5	-0.25	0	0.25	0.5	0.75	1	2
y	8		1.13		0.13		0.13		1.13		

THIS IS FOUND BY WORKING OUT $2 \times (-0.75)^2 = 1.13$ *TO 2 d.p.*

b) Use graph paper and draw axes for the ranges $-3 \leqslant x \leqslant 3$ and $-1 \leqslant y \leqslant 9$. Use 2 cm for 1 unit on each axis.

c) Plot the points and draw a smooth curve through them.

d) Use your graph to find the value of y when $x = 1.5$.

e) Check you answer to (d) by finding the value of y when $x = 1.5$ from the equation $y = 2x^2$.

3. The equation of a curve is $y = 2 - x^2$.

a) Copy and complete this table to give the coordinates of some points on the curve.

x	-3	-2	-1.5	-1	-0.5	0	0.5	1	1.5	2	3
y	-7	-2	-0.25	1	1.75				-0.25		

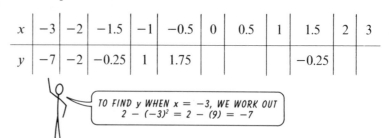

TO FIND y WHEN $x = -3$, WE WORK OUT
$2 - (-3)^2 = 2 - (9) = -7$

b) Using graph paper, draw axes for the ranges $-4 \leqslant x \leqslant 4$ and $-8 \leqslant y \leqslant 3$.

c) Plot the points and draw a smooth curve through them.

d) Use your graph to find the value of y when $x = 1.6$.

e) This graph has a line of symmetry. What is this line?

f) What is the greatest value of y on your graph?

4. The equation of a line is $y = 2x - 1$.

a) Copy and complete this table to give the coordinates of some points on the curve.

x	-2	0	2
y			

b) On the graph that you used for question 3, plot these points and draw the line.

c) Write down the coordinates of the points where the line and the curve cross.

5. The equation of a curve is $y = x^2 - 1$.

a) Make a table to give the coordinates of some points on this curve using values of x from -3 to 3.

b) Use graph paper and a scale of 2 cm for 1 unit on each axis and plot the points.

c) If you have enough points to "see" a smooth curve through them, draw the curve. If there are not enough points, work out the coordinates of some more points and then draw the curve.

d) Write two sentences describing how you can use the value of y when $x = 2.5$ to check the shape of your curve near that point.

25 AREAS

REVISION OF BASIC UNITS

Units of length The basic unit of length is the metre (m).
Other units in common use are the centimetre (cm),
the millimetre (mm) and the kilometre (km), where

$$1 \text{ km} = 1000 \text{ m}$$

$$1 \text{ m} = 100 \text{ cm} \qquad \vdash\!\!\!-\!\!\!\dashv \; 1 \text{ cm}$$

$$1 \text{ cm} = 10 \text{ mm}$$

EXERCISE 25a

> Express 2.5 m in centimetres.
>
> $$2.5 \text{ m} = 2.5 \times 100 \text{ cm}$$
> $$= 250 \text{ cm}$$

Express the given quantity in the unit in brackets.

1. 5.3 km (m)	**4.** 52 cm (mm)	**7.** 18 cm (mm)
2. 2.8 cm (mm)	**5.** 5 m (mm)	**8.** 2 m (mm)
3. 1.7 m (cm)	**6.** 2.3 m (cm)	**9.** 8.7 km (m)

> Express 57 cm in metres.
>
> $$57 \text{ cm} = 57 \div 100 \text{ m}$$
> $$= 0.57 \text{ m}$$

Express the given quantity in the unit in brackets.

10. 250 mm (cm)

11. 50 cm (m)

12. 1000 m (km)

13. 350 mm (cm)

14. 2500 m (km)

15. 872 mm (cm)

16. 2850 m (km)

17. 28 mm (cm)

18. 180 m (km)

19. 650 cm (m)

PERIMETERS

The perimeter of a plane figure is the distance all round it, i.e. the sum of the lengths of its sides.

EXERCISE 25b

Find the perimeter of the given figure.

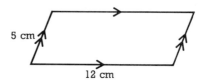

(This is a parallelogram, so the opposite sides are equal in length.)

Perimeter = (5 + 12 + 5 + 12) cm

= 34 cm

Find the perimeter of each of the following figures.

1.

2.

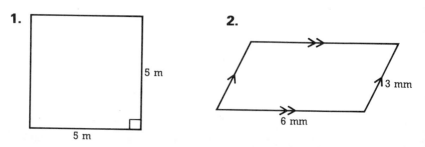

3.

1.5 cm

6 cm

8.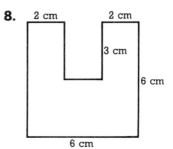

2 cm   2 cm

3 cm

6 cm

6 cm

4.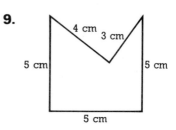

25 m

7 m

24 m

9.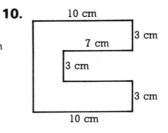

4 cm 3 cm

5 cm   5 cm

5 cm

5.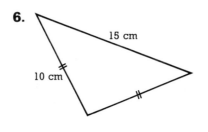

10 cm

4 cm   4 cm

12 cm

10.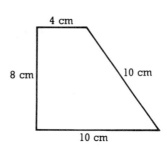

10 cm

3 cm

7 cm

3 cm

3 cm

10 cm

6.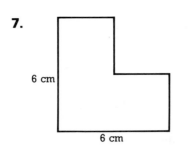

15 cm

10 cm

11.

4 cm

8 cm   10 cm

10 cm

7.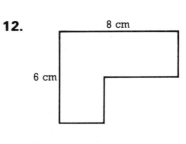

6 cm

6 cm

12.

8 cm

6 cm

THE AREA OF A RECTANGLE

The area of a rectangle is found by multiplying its length by its breadth.

$$A = l \times b$$

A square is a rectangle whose length and breadth are the same.

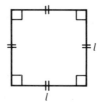

$$A = l \times l$$
$$= l^2$$

EXERCISE 25c Remember that area is measured in square units.

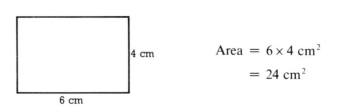

Find the area of a rectangle measuring 6 cm by 4 cm.

4 cm

6 cm

Area $= 6 \times 4 \text{ cm}^2$

$= 24 \text{ cm}^2$

Find the area of each of the following shapes. Remember that you must state the units involved.

1. A square of side 8 m.

2. A rectangle measuring 4 cm by 3 cm.

3. A square of side 2 mm.

4. A rectangle measuring 4 m by 8 m.

5. A rectangle measuring 10 m by 12 m.

6. A square of side 5 cm.

7. A rectangle of length 20 mm and breadth 8 mm.

8. A rectangle measuring 1.5 cm by 4 cm.

9. A square of side 2.5 m.

10. A rectangle measuring 1.2 cm by 2.3 cm.

Remember that, when we find an area, the measurements that we use must be in the *same* unit. We usually change the larger unit to the smaller unit.

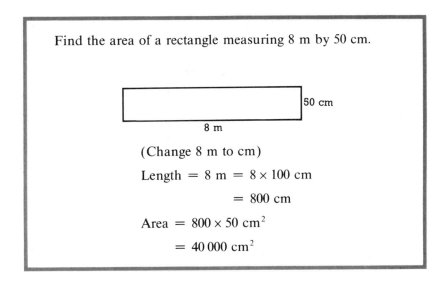

Find the area of a rectangle measuring 8 m by 50 cm.

50 cm

8 m

(Change 8 m to cm)

Length $= 8$ m $= 8 \times 100$ cm

$= 800$ cm

Area $= 800 \times 50$ cm^2

$= 40\,000$ cm^2

Find the areas of the following rectangles.

11. Length 1 cm, breadth 5 mm.

12. Length 1 m, breadth 20 cm.

13. Length 0.5 cm, breadth 3 mm.

14. Length 1 m, breadth 30 cm.

15. Length 2 cm, breadth 4 mm.

16. Length 3 m, breadth 70 cm.

17. Length 10 cm, breadth 9 mm.

18. Length 0.3 m, breadth 22 cm.

19. Length 100 mm, breadth 0.4 cm.

20. Length 200 cm, breadth 0.6 m.

THE AREA OF A TRIANGLE

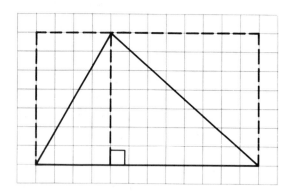

If we enclose a triangle in a rectangle we can see that the area of the triangle is half the area of the rectangle.

However, the length of the rectangle is the same as the length of the base of the triangle and the breadth of the rectangle is the same as the perpendicular height of the triangle.

∴   Area of triangle $= \frac{1}{2} \times$ base $\times$ perpendicular height

EXERCISE 25d

Find the area of the triangle in the diagram.

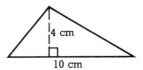

$$\text{Area} = \tfrac{1}{2} \times \text{base} \times \text{perpendicular height}$$
$$= 0.5 \times 10 \times 4 \text{ cm}^2$$
$$= 20 \text{ cm}^2$$

Find the areas of the following triangles.

1.

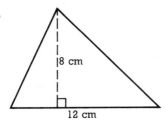

4.

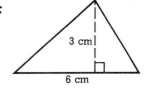

2.

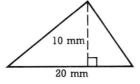

5.

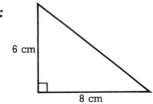

3.

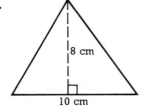

6.

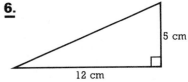

7.

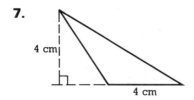

4 cm

4 cm

9.

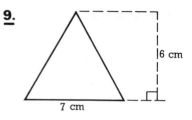

6 cm

7 cm

8.

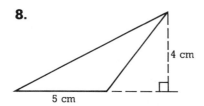

4 cm

5 cm

10.

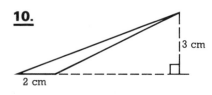

3 cm

2 cm

In questions 11 to 16 turn the page round if necessary so that you can see which is the base and which is the perpendicular height.

11.

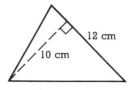

12 cm

10 cm

14.

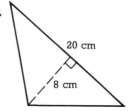

20 cm

8 cm

12.

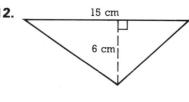

15 cm

6 cm

15.

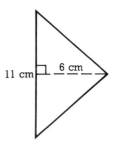

11 cm

6 cm

13.

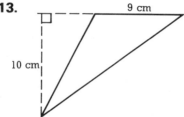

9 cm

10 cm

16.

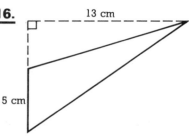

13 cm

5 cm

AREAS OF COMPOUND SHAPES

It is often possible to find the area of a figure by dividing it into two or more shapes whose areas can be found.

For example, this shape can be divided into two rectangles

and this one can be divided into a square and a triangle.

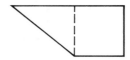

EXERCISE 25e

Find the area of the figure in the diagram.

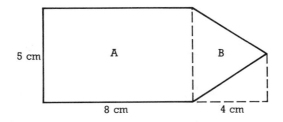

(A is a rectangle, 8 cm by 5 cm
B is a triangle, base 5 cm, height 4 cm.)

Area of A $= 8 \times 5$ cm^2

$\qquad = 40$ cm^2

Area of B $= \frac{1}{2} \times$ base $\times$ perpendicular height

$\qquad = 0.5 \times 5 \times 4$ cm^2

$\qquad = 10$ cm^2

Therefore the total area $= 50$ cm^2

In questions 1 to 6, each figure is divided into two shapes A and B. In each case

a) copy the figure,

b) name the shapes A and B and mark any extra measurements needed to find the areas,

c) find the area of A,

d) find the area of B,

e) find the total area of the figure.

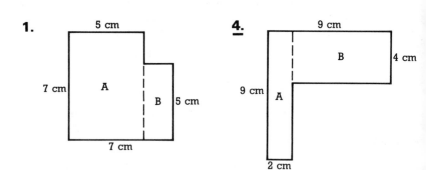

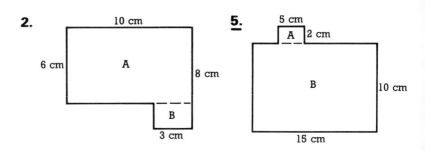

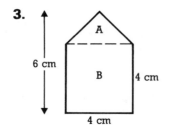
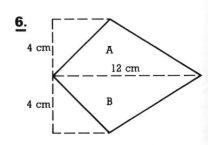

For the given figure find
a) the perimeter
b) the area.

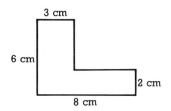

(From the measurements given we can work out the lengths of the other sides.)

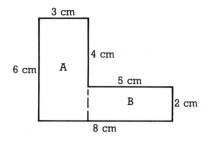

a)   Perimeter = $(6 + 3 + 4 + 5 + 2 + 8)$ cm

                    = 28 cm

b)   Area of A = 6×3 cm^2

                    = 18 cm^2

            Area of B = 5×2 cm^2

                    = 10 cm^2

            Total area = $(18 + 10)$ cm^2 = 28 cm^2

In each of the following questions find
a) the perimeter   b) the area   of the given figure.

7.

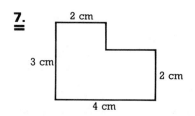

8.

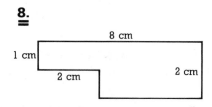

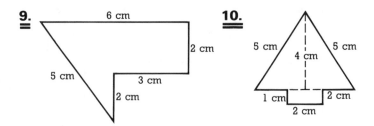

THE AREA OF A PARALLELOGRAM

We can find the area of a parallelogram by dividing it into two triangles which have bases of equal length and equal perpendicular heights.

EXERCISE 25f

Find the area of the parallelogram in the diagram.

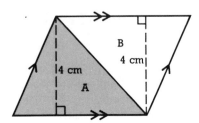

(We divide the parallelogram into two triangles by drawing a diagonal.)

$$\text{Area of triangle A} = \tfrac{1}{2} \times 8 \times 4 \text{ cm}^2$$
$$= 16 \text{ cm}^2$$

(Now turn the page upside down.)

$$\text{Area of triangle B} = \tfrac{1}{2} \times 8 \times 4 \text{ cm}^2$$
$$= 16 \text{ cm}^2$$

$$\text{Area of parallelogram} = \text{area A} + \text{area B}$$
$$= 16 \text{ cm}^2 + 16 \text{ cm}^2$$
$$= 32 \text{ cm}^2$$

Find the areas of the following parallelograms.

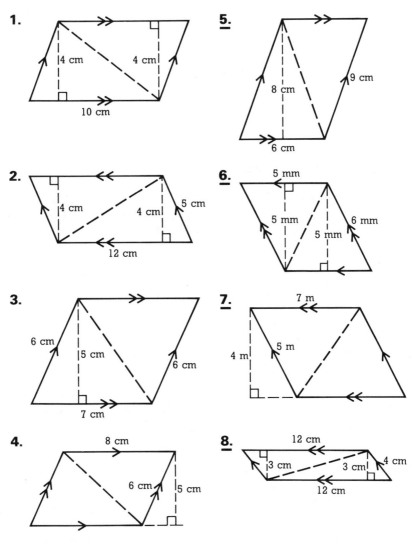

1. 4 cm, 4 cm, 10 cm

5. 8 cm, 9 cm, 6 cm

2. 4 cm, 4 cm, 5 cm, 12 cm

6. 5 mm, 5 mm, 5 mm, 6 mm

3. 6 cm, 5 cm, 6 cm, 7 cm

7. 7 m, 5 m, 4 m

4. 8 cm, 6 cm, 5 cm

8. 12 cm, 3 cm, 3 cm, 4 cm, 12 cm

In questions 9 to 12 you may find it an advantage to turn the page around so that the base of each triangle is in its usual position.

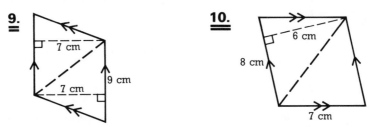

9. 7 cm, 7 cm, 9 cm

10. 6 cm, 8 cm, 7 cm

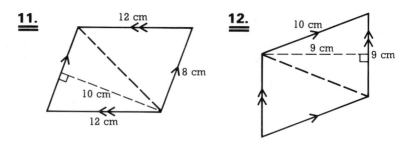

11. 12 cm / 8 cm / 10 cm / 12 cm

12. 10 cm / 9 cm / 9 cm

THE AREA OF A TRAPEZIUM

The area of a trapezium can also be found by drawing a diagonal to divide the shape into two triangles. This time, although the two triangles have the same height the lengths of their bases are different.

EXERCISE 25g

Find the area of this trapezium.

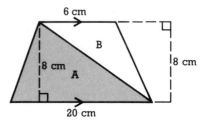

6 cm / B / 8 cm / 8 cm / A / 20 cm

(We divide the trapezium into two triangles by drawing a diagonal.)

$$\text{Area of triangle A} = \tfrac{1}{2} \times 20 \times 8 \text{ cm}^2$$
$$= 80 \text{ cm}^2$$

(Now turn the page upside down.)

$$\text{Area of triangle B} = \tfrac{1}{2} \times 6 \times 8 \text{ cm}^2$$
$$= 24 \text{ cm}^2$$

$$\text{Area of trapezium} = \text{area A} + \text{area B}$$
$$= 80 \text{ cm}^2 + 24 \text{ cm}^2$$
$$= 104 \text{ cm}^2$$

Find the areas of the following trapeziums.

1.

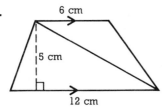

2.

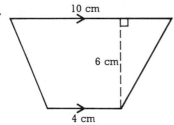

3.

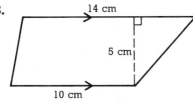

4.

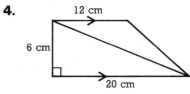

5.

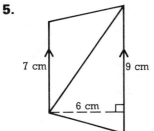

6.

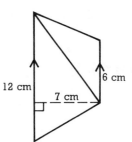

7.

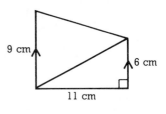

8.

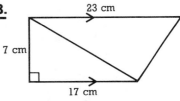

9.

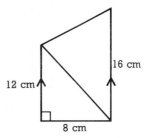

10.

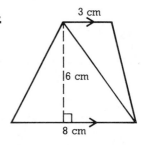

MIXED QUESTIONS ══

Remember that "height" means "perpendicular height".

EXERCISE 25h The shapes in this exercise are drawn on squared paper. Each square is of side 0.5 cm. Copy each figure on to squared paper and for each question

a) name the shape.

b) on your diagram mark the lengths (in cm) of the lines you need to find its area. (You may need to draw a diagonal to divide the shape into two triangles.)

c) find the area of the shape in cm².

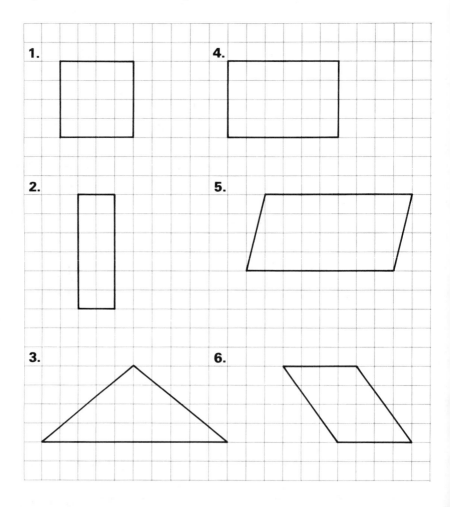

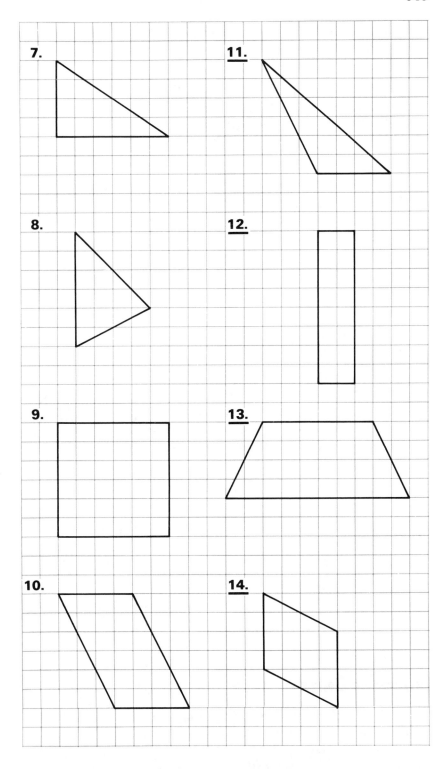

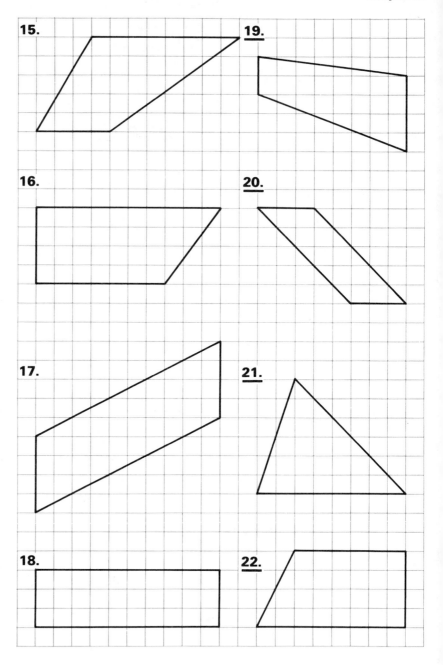

CHANGING UNITS OF AREA

Sometimes we wish to change from one unit of area to another, e.g. from mm^2 to cm^2 or from cm^2 to m^2.

A square of side 1 cm can be divided into 100 equal squares of side 1 mm,

$$\text{i.e.} \quad 1 \text{ cm}^2 = 100 \text{ mm}^2$$

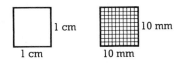

Similarly since   1 m = 100 cm

$$1 \text{ square metre} = 100 \times 100 \text{ square centimetres}$$
$$\text{i.e.} \quad 1 \text{ m}^2 = 10\,000 \text{ cm}^2$$

and as   1 km = 1000 m

$$1 \text{ km}^2 = 1000 \times 1000 \text{ m}^2$$
$$\text{i.e.} \quad 1 \text{ km}^2 = 1\,000\,000 \text{ m}^2$$

When we convert from a unit of area which is large to a unit of area which is smaller we must remember that the number of units will be bigger,

$$\text{e.g.} \quad 2 \text{ km}^2 = 2 \times 1\,000\,000 \text{ m}^2$$
$$= 2\,000\,000 \text{ m}^2$$

$$\text{and} \quad 12 \text{ m}^2 = 12 \times 10\,000 \text{ cm}^2$$
$$= 120\,000 \text{ cm}^2$$

while if we convert from a unit of area which is small into one which is larger the number of units will be smaller,

$$\text{e.g.} \quad 500 \text{ mm}^2 = \frac{500}{100} \text{ cm}^2$$
$$= 5 \text{ cm}^2$$

In the metric system, areas of land are measured in hectares. A square of side 100 m has an area of 1 hectare.

Hence $1 \text{ hectare} = 100 \times 100 \text{ m}^2$

i.e. $1 \text{ ha} = 10\,000 \text{ m}^2$

EXERCISE 25i

> Express 5 m^2 in   a) cm^2 b) mm^2
>
>
> a)   Since   1 m^2 = 100 × 100 cm^2
>
>   5 m^2 = 5 × 100 × 100 cm^2
>
>   = 50 000 cm^2
>
> b)   Since   1 cm^2 = 100 mm^2
>
>   50 000 cm^2 = 50 000 × 100 mm^2
>
>
> Therefore   5 m^2 = 50 000 cm^2 = 5 000 000 mm^2.

1.   Express in cm^2
       a) 3 m^2 b) 12 m^2 c) 7.5 m^2 d) 82 m^2 e) 8.5 m^2

2.   Express in mm^2
       a) 14 cm^2 b) 3 cm^2 c) 7.5 cm^2 d) 26 cm^2 e) 32.5 cm^2

3.   Express 0.056 m^2 in   a) cm^2 b) mm^2.

Express the given quantity in the unit in brackets.

4. 5 cm^2 (mm^2)   **8.** 3 cm^2 (mm^2)

5. 2 ha (m^2)   **9.** 0.5 m^2 (mm^2)

6. 0.2 m^2 (cm^2)   **10.** 2.6 cm^2 (mm^2)

7. 0.5 cm^2 (mm^2)   **11.** 5.5 ha (m^2)

> Express 25 000 m^2 in hectares.
>
>
> Since   1 hectare = 10 000 m^2
>
>   25 000 m^2 = 25 000 ÷ 10 000 ha
>
>   = 2.5 ha

Express the given quantity in the unit in brackets.

12. 300 mm² (cm²)   **17.** 560 cm² (m²)

13. 50 000 m² (ha)   **18.** 5680 mm² (cm²)

14. 2500 cm² (m²)   **19.** 40 800 m² (ha)

15. 5000 m (km)   **20.** 650 cm (m)

16. 2.7 cm (mm)   **21.** 80 000 m² (ha)

22. 36 cm² (mm²)   **26.** 2.5 km² (m²)

23. 5.3 mm (cm)   **27.** 0.5 cm (mm)

24. 380 cm (m)   **28.** 500 mm² (cm²)

25. 9.8 m (cm)   **29.** 82 cm (m)

30. . The page of a book measures 140 mm by 250 mm.
Find its area   a) in mm²   b) in cm².

31. A rectangular playing area measures 300 m by 450 m.
Find its area   a) in m²   b) in hectares.

32. The squares on a draughts board are of side 35 mm.
Find the area of one square   a) in mm²   b) in cm².
If there are 64 squares altogether find the total area of the
board in cm².

PROBLEMS

EXERCISE 25j 1. The diagram represents a rectangular sports ground. The shaded
area is a rectangular pitch.

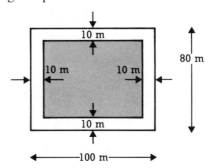

(The arrowheads show that the border is 10 m wide.)

For the pitch, find
a) the length   b) the width   c) the perimeter   d) the area.

2.   The diagram shows the layout of a rectangular garden.
The shaded area is a paved patio, the rest is grass.

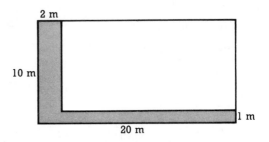

Find   a) the perimeter of the whole garden

b) the length of the lawn

c) the width of the lawn

d) the area of the lawn

e) the area of the patio

f) the perimeter of the lawn.

3.   The diagram shows the end wall of a garden shed.
The shaded area is a door.

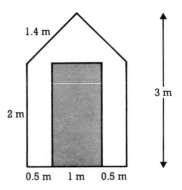

Find   a) the width of the wall

b) the area of the wall, including the door

c) the area of the door

d) the area of the unshaded part of the wall.

4. The diagram represents a rectangular allotment.
The shaded area is path, the rest is a vegetable plot.

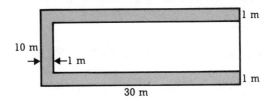

Find a) the length of the vegetable plot

        b) the width of the vegetable plot

        c) the area of the vegetable plot

        d) the area of the whole allotment

        e) the area of the path

        f) the perimeter of the vegetable plot

        g) the perimeter of the shaded area.

5. The diagram shows the floor plan of a room.
The shaded area is carpet, the rest is polished wood.

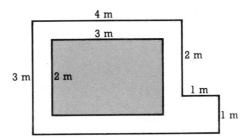

Find the area a) of the carpet

               b) of the whole floor

               c) of the uncarpeted part of the floor.

26 CIRCLE CALCULATIONS

RADIUS, DIAMETER AND CIRCUMFERENCE

These diagrams give a reminder of the names of the parts of a circle.

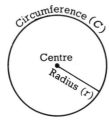 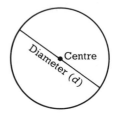

A diameter goes through the centre of a circle so it is twice as long as a radius,

i.e.

$$d = 2r$$

EXERCISE 26a Write down the length of the diameter of each of the following circles.

1.

2 mm

4.
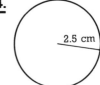
2.5 cm

2.

4 cm

5.

3 mm

3.
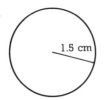
1.5 cm

6.
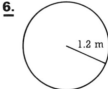
1.2 m

Write down the length of the radius of each of the following circles.

7.

6 cm

9.

5 cm

8.

4 mm

10.
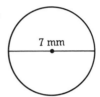
7 mm

THE CIRCUMFERENCE OF A CIRCLE

In Book 2B we saw that, whatever the size of the circle, the circumference is just over three times the length of the diameter.

To get the circumference we have to multiply the diameter by a number that is a little bigger than 3. We cannot write this number exactly using figures so we call it π (pronounced "pie").

Therefore   circumference $= \pi \times$ diameter

or $C = \pi d$

or $C = 2\pi r$

where r is the radius.

To as many figures as we can write across the page

$\pi = 3.14159265358979323846264338327950288419716939937510582097$

Luckily we never need this degree of this accuracy! If you have a scientific calculator, use the π button in calculations. If your calculator does not have a π button, use 3.142 for the value of π. In either case give answers correct to 3 s.f.

EXERCISE 26b If only a rough approximation is needed we can take 3 as the value for π.

A circle has a radius of 4 cm. Taking $\pi = 3$, find the approximate length of the circumference of the circle.

$C = 2\pi r$

$2\pi r = 2 \times 3 \times 4$ cm

$\qquad = 24$ cm

The circumference is approximately 24 cm.

4 cm

In each question from 1 to 9, use $\pi = 3$ to find an approximate value for the circumference of a circle, whose radius is

1. 6 cm	**4.** 3 m	**7.** 10 m
2. 2 cm	**5.** 2 mm	**8.** 30 m
3. 4 cm	**6.** 8 m	**9.** 12 m

10. The diameter of a ventilation shaft is 1 m. Find an approximate value for the circumference of the shaft.

Use a calculator to find the circumference of a circle whose radius is 5.6 cm. (If your calculator does not have a π button use 3.142 for π.)

$C = 2\pi r$

$\quad = 2 \times \pi \times 5.6$ cm   ($\boxed{2}$ $\boxed{\times}$ $\boxed{\pi}$ $\boxed{\times}$ $\boxed{5}$ $\boxed{\cdot}$ $\boxed{6}$ $\boxed{=}$)

$\quad = 35.19$ cm

The circumference is 35.2 cm correct to 3 s.f.

For the following questions use a calculator and give your answers correct to three significant figures.

Find the circumference of a circle of radius

11. 38 mm	**14.** 3.5 cm	**17.** 12.6 cm
12. 4.4 m	**15.** 2.6 cm	**18.** 9.3 cm
13. 8.2 m	**16.** 10.5 cm	**19.** 315 cm

Find   a) the radius   b) the circumference
of a circle of whose *diameter* is

20. 56 cm	**23.** 14 cm	**26.** 6.3 cm
21. 8.4 cm	**24.** 2.8 cm	**27.** 2.1 cm
22. 98 cm	**25.** 3.5 cm	**28.** 42 cm

SECTIONS OF A CIRCLE

Half a circle is called a *semicircle*.

One quarter of a circle is called a *quadrant*.

Part of the circumference of a circle is called an *arc*.

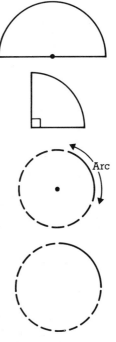

This is a semicircular arc. Its length is half of the circumference of the whole circle.

This is a quadrant arc. Its length is one quarter of the circumference of the whole circle.

EXERCISE 26c

The goal area of a hockey pitch is marked out by a line in the shape of a semicircle of radius 16 yards.
Find the length of the line.

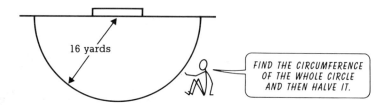

Circumference of whole circle $= 2\pi r$

$$= 2 \times \pi \times 16 \text{ yards}$$

$$= 100.53 \ldots \text{ yards}$$

Length of line round goal area $= 100.53 \div 2 \text{ yards}$

$$= 50.26 \ldots \text{ yards}$$

Length of line is 50.3 yards correct to 3 s.f.

1. A semicircular protractor has a radius of 5 cm. Find, correct to 3 s.f., the distance round the curved edge.

2. A fan is in the shape of a quadrant of a circle of radius 12 cm.
Find the length of the curved edge.

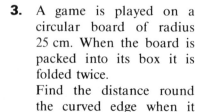

3. A game is played on a circular board of radius 25 cm. When the board is packed into its box it is folded twice.
Find the distance round the curved edge when it has been folded

a) once   b) twice

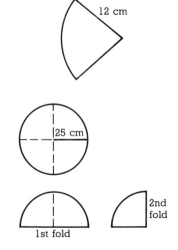

The cross-section of a plastic moulding is a quadrant of a circle of radius 2 cm. Find the perimeter of the cross-section.

(AB and AC are each of length 2 cm because they are both radii of the circle. We will have to calculate the length of the arc BC.)

The arc BC is a quarter of the circumference of a circle of radius 2 cm.

$$\text{Circumference of whole circle} = 2\pi r$$
$$= 2 \times \pi \times 2 \text{ cm}$$
$$= 12.568 \text{ cm}$$
$$\therefore \quad \text{length of arc BC} = 12.568 \div 4 \text{ cm}$$
$$= 3.142 \text{ cm}$$

$$\text{Perimeter of cross-section} = AB + AC + BC$$
$$= 2 + 2 + 3.142 \text{ cm}$$
$$= 7.142 \text{ cm}$$
$$= 7.14 \text{ cm} \quad \text{correct to 3 s.f.}$$

In questions 4 to 10 give answers correct to three significant figures.

4.

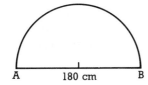

A semicircular hearth rug has a diameter of 180 cm. Find

a) the radius of the semicircle
b) the length of the arc AB
c) the perimeter of the rug.

5.

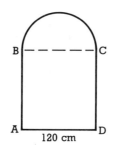

A window is in the shape of a square with a semicircle on the top. Find

a) the lengths of BC, AB and DC
b) the radius of the semicircle
c) the length of the arc BC
d) the perimeter of the window.

6.

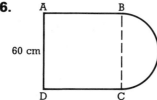

A kitchen worktop is a square with a semicircle on one end. Find

a) the radius of the semicircle
b) the length of the arc BC
c) the perimeter of the worktop.

7.

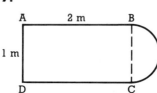

The diagram shows a rectangular breakfast bar with a semicircular flap at the end. Find

a) the length of BC
b) the radius of the semicircle
c) the length of the arc BC
d) the perimeter of the breakfast bar.

8.

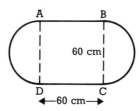

The diagram shows a model railway track. The ends are semicircles. Find

a) the radius of each semicircle
b) the lengths of the arcs AD and BC
c) the perimeter of the figure.

9.

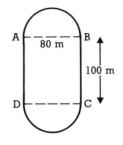

A Speedway track with semicircular ends is shown in the diagram. Find

a) the radius of each semicircle
b) the lengths of the arcs AB and CD
c) the perimeter of the figure.

10.

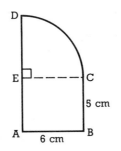

The figure shows the cross-section of a plinth for a cupboard. Find

a) the lengths of EC and AD
b) the length of the arc DC
c) the perimeter of the figure.

THE AREA OF A CIRCLE

The formula for finding the area, A, of a circle is

$$A = \pi r^2$$

You can see where this formula comes from if you imagine a circle cut into narrow slices.

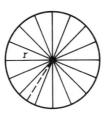

When the slices are put together again as shown we get a "rectangle" with the same area as the circle.

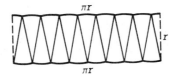

The length is half the circumference of the circle and the width is the radius of the circle.
So the area of the rectangle is $\pi r \times r = \pi r^2$

Therefore the area of a circle $= \pi r^2$

EXERCISE 26d

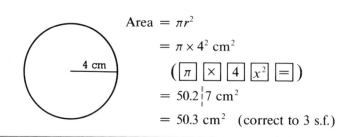

Find the area of a circle of radius 4 cm.

4 cm

Area $= \pi r^2$

$= \pi \times 4^2$ cm^2

($\boxed{\pi}$ $\boxed{\times}$ $\boxed{4}$ $\boxed{x^2}$ $\boxed{=}$)

$= 50.2\vert 7$ cm^2

$= 50.3$ cm^2 (correct to 3 s.f.)

Use a calculator to find the area of each of the following circles. Give your answers to three significant figures.

1.
2 cm

5.
1 cm

9.
5.6 cm

2.
3 cm

6.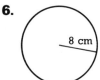
8 cm

10.
56 mm

3.
5 cm

7.
1.4 cm

11.
63 mm

4.
6 cm

8.
2.8 cm

12.
4.2 cm

EXERCISE 26e

Find the area of a semi-circular flower bed whose radius is 1.2 cm.

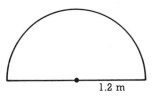

(The area of this semicircle is half of the area of the whole circle.)

1.2 m

Area of whole circle $= \pi r^2$

$= \pi \times (1.2)^2 \text{ m}^2$

$= 4.5239 \text{ m}^2$

Area of flower bed $= 4.524 \div 2 \text{ m}^2$

$= 2.26 \vert 2 \text{ m}^2$

$= 2.26 \text{ m}^2$ (correct to 3 s.f.)

Give your answers correct to 3 s.f.

1.

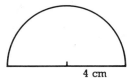

4 cm

The radius of this protractor is 4 cm.
Find its area.

2.

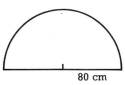

80 cm

The radius of this semi-circular hall table is 80 cm. What is its area?

3.

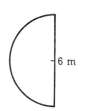

6 m

The shape of this flower bed is a semicircle of *diameter* 6 m. Find

a) its radius
b) its area.

4.

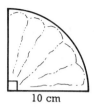

10 cm

Extra-Krisp biscuits are quadrant shaped. Find the area of a biscuit.

5.

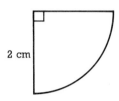

2 cm

The diagram shows the cross-section of a window moulding. Find its area.

6.

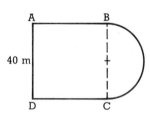

40 m

The floor of a concert hall is square and the stage is a semicircle. Find

a) the area of floor
b) the area of the stage
c) the total area.

7.

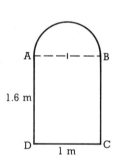

1.6 m

1 m

A door is made up of a rectangle ABCD with a semicircular top.

a) Find the area of the rectangular part.
b) Give the radius of the semicircle.
c) Find the area of the semicircle.
d) What is the area of the whole door?

8.

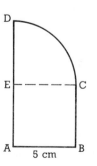

5 cm

The diagram shows a quadrant on one side of a square. Find

a) the area of the square
b) the area of the quadrant
c) the area of the whole figure.

9. 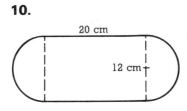 The diagram shows two circles with the same centre. The radius of the larger circle is 10 cm and the radius of the smaller circle is 4 cm. Find

a) the area of the larger circle
b) the area of the smaller circle
c) the shaded area between the two circles.

10. The diagram shows a rectangle with semicircles on the two short ends. Find

a) the area of the rectangle
b) the radius of each semicircle
c) the area of each semicircle
d) the area of the whole figure.

PROBLEMS

EXERCISE 26f Give your answers correct to 3 s.f.

1.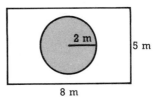

The diagram represents a rectangular lawn with a circular flower bed in the middle.

Find   a) the area of the whole plot

b) the area of the flower bed

c) the area of the grassed part of the plot. (Use your answers to (a) and (b).)

d) the circumference of the flower bed

e) the number of bedding plants that can be placed round the edge of the flower bed if they have to be planted 0.5 m apart. (Use your answer to (d).)

2.

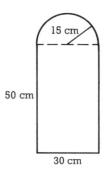

15 cm

50 cm

30 cm

The diagram shows an arched window. The lower part is a rectangle measuring 30 cm by 50 cm. The upper part is a semicircle of radius 15 cm.

Find a) the total height of the window
           b) the area of the rectangular part of the window
           c) the area of the semicircular part of the window
           d) the total area of the window correct to 3 s.f.
           e) the cost of glass to glaze the window if glass costs 0.6 p per cm^2 (Use your answer to (d).)
           f) the perimeter of the window.

3.

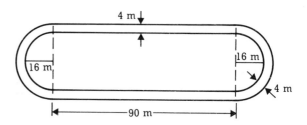

4 m

16 m

16 m

4 m

90 m

The diagram shows a running track which is 4 m wide. The straight sides are each 90 cm long. The radius of each *inner* semicircular end is 16 m.

Find a) the length of each *inner* semicircular arc
           b) the perimeter of the *inside* of the track
           c) the radius of each *outer* semicircular arc
           d) the length of each *outer* semicircular arc
           e) the perimeter of the *outside* of the track
           f) the difference between the distance run by an athlete keeping to the outside of the track and the distance run by another athlete keeping to the inside of the track. (Use your answers to (b) and (e).)

27 SIMULTANEOUS EQUATIONS

Sometimes we find that we have letters standing for *two* unknown numbers in an equation.

If we are told that $x + y = 6$, then we could have x as 2 and y as 4 but there are other possibilities: for example, we could have x as 3 and y as 3.

EXERCISE 27a 1. Two numbers add up to 14. Give two possible pairs of numbers.

2. Two numbers add up to 9. Give three possible pairs of numbers.

3. I think of two numbers. I take the second number from the first and get 2. Give one set of possible values for the numbers.

4. Karen and Brian between them have 12 apples.

a) How many apples might they each have?

b) How many possibilities are there of different pairs? Give a list of the pairs.

Find three possibilities for the pairs of values of x and y if $x - y = 8$.

$$10 - 2 = 8 \quad \text{so} \quad x = 10 \quad \text{and} \quad y = 2$$
$$8 - 0 = 8 \quad \text{so} \quad x = 8 \quad \text{and} \quad y = 0$$
$$12 - 4 = 8 \quad \text{so} \quad x = 12 \quad \text{and} \quad y = 4$$

(There are many other possibilities.)

In each case, find three possible pairs of values for x and y.

5. $x + y = 16$ **8.** $y - x = 7$

6. $x - y = 4$ **9.** $x + 3y = 12$

7. $2x + y = 9$ **10.** $2x + 3y = 30$

If $3x + 2y = 9$ and $x = 1$, what is y?

$$3x + 2y = 9$$
$$x = 1, \text{ so } 3 + 2y = 9$$

Take 3 from each side $2y = 6$

Divide both sides by 2 $y = 3$

---

11. If $x + y = 20$ and $y = 12$, find x.

12. If $a - b = 8$ and $b = 4$, find a.

13. If $2p + q = 10$ and $p = 3$, find q.

14. If $x - 2y = 2$ and $y = 4$, find x.

15. If $3a - c = 4$ and $c = 8$, find a.

16. If $3x + 4y = 18$ and $x = 2$, find y.

17. If $2a + b = 18$ and $b = 4$, find a.

18. If $2p + 3q = 18$ and $p = 3$, find q.

CHECKING SOLUTIONS

Do $x = 6$ and $y = 7$ fit the equation $3x - 2y = 4$?

If $x = 6$ and $y = 7$, $\quad 3x - 2y = 3 \times 6 - 2 \times 7$

$$= 18 - 14$$

$$= 4$$

They do fit the equation.

In each case find out whether the given values of x and y fit the equation.

1. $x + y = 11$, $x = 6$, $y = 5$

2. $2x - y = 3$, $x = 3$, $y = 1$

3. $2x + 3y = 5$, $x = 1$, $y = 2$

4. $3x - 2y = 7$, $x = 3$, $y = 1$

5. $4x + y = 18$, $x = 2$, $y = 1$

Do $x = 4$ and $y = 1$ fit both of the equations

$2x - y = 7$ and $2x + y = 11$

If $x = 4$ and $y = 1$, $\quad 2x - y = 2 \times 4 - 1$

$$= 8 - 1$$

$$= 7 \qquad \qquad \text{Correct}$$

$$2x + y = 8 + 1$$

$$= 9 \qquad \qquad \text{Not correct}$$

They do not fit both equations.

In each case find out whether the given values of x and y fit *both* equations.

6. $x + y = 6$

$x - y = 4$

$x = 4,\ y = 2$

7. $x - y = 7$

$x + y = 10$

$x = 9,\ y = 2$

8. $x + 2y = 5$

$2x + y = 9$

$x = 4,\ y = 1$

9. $x - y = 2$

$2x - y = 1$

$x = 1,\ y = 3$

10. $2x + 3y = 17$

$x + y = 7$

$x = 4,\ y = 3$

11. $3x - y = 10$

$x + 4y = 12$

$x = 4,\ y = 2$

TWO UNKNOWN NUMBERS, TWO EQUATIONS

If we have only one letter standing for an unknown number, and one equation such as $3x = 12$, we can find that number.

If we have two letters standing for unknown numbers and only one equation, we have seen that we cannot pin down the two numbers. There are usually many possibilities.

We need two equations if we wish to find two unknown numbers.

Guesswork will sometimes find the answer.

$$x + y = 6$$
$$x - y = 4$$

Try $x = 4$ and $y = 2$. These fit the first equation but not the second one.

Try $x = 5$ and $y = 1$. These fit both equations so we now know that x is 5 and y is 1.

Although it does sometimes work, guesswork is not the best way. We need a more organised method.

REDUCING TWO EQUATIONS TO ONE

Consider this pair of equations: $3x + y = 5$ [1]

$$x + y = 3 \quad [2]$$

If we can get rid of one letter, we will make an equation with just the remaining letter and we know how to solve this.

Each equation has the same number of y's, so if we take one equation from the other, the y's will go.

$$3x + y = 5 \quad [1]$$
$$\underline{x + y = 3} \quad [2]$$

[1] − [2] gives $2x \quad\ = 2$

EXERCISE 27c

Use the two equations below to give one equation in x.

$$4x + 2y = 14$$
$$x + 2y = 5$$

$$4x + 2y = 14 \quad [1] \quad \text{(Number the equations.)}$$
$$x + 2y = 5 \quad [2]$$

(There are the same number of y's in each equation so if we subtract, the y's will disappear.)

[1] − [2] gives $3x = 9$

Use each pair of equations to give one equation. Remember to number the equations first.

1. $5x + y = 6$ **3.** $4x + 3y = 7$

$3x + y = 4$ $2x + 3y = 5$

2. $6p + 2q = 14$ **4.** $5a + b = 7$

$3p + 2q = 8$ $2a + b = 3$

Sometimes the first equation has to be taken from the second.

Find one equation from each pair.

5. $4x + y = 9$

$7x + y = 15$

7. $3p + 2q = 7$

$5p + 2q = 9$

6. $x + y = 7$

$3x + y = 11$

8. $a + b = 11$

$4a + b = 29$

SOLVING A PAIR OF EQUATIONS

Two equations with two unknown numbers to find are called *simultaneous equations*. ("Simultaneous" means "happening at the same time", so the two numbers must fit both equations at the same time.)

EXERCISE 27d

Solve the pair of equations $2x + y = 8$

$x + y = 6$

$2x + y = 8$ [1]

$x + y = 6$ [2]

(We want to get rid of one of the letters.)

Take equation [2] from equation [1].

(If we take y from y there are no y's left.)

$$x = 2$$

(Looking at [2] we see that if $x = 2$ then $y = 4$)

Using [2], $y = 4$

(Now we must check in the other equation, i.e. [1], to make sure we are right.)

In [1], if $x = 2$ and $y = 4$, $2x + y = 4 + 4$

$$= 8 \quad \text{(correct)}$$

so $x = 2$ and $y = 4$

Solve the following pairs of equations by taking the second from the first.

1. $3z + y = 8$ [1]
   $z + y = 4$ [2]

2. $4p + q = 14$ [1]
   $2p + q = 8$ [2]

3. $2x + 3y = 13$ [1]
   $x + 3y = 11$ [2]

4. $2a + b = 5$ [1]
   $a + b = 4$ [2]

Solve the following equations by taking the first from the second.

5. $x + y = 11$ [1]
   $2x + y = 12$ [2]

6. $p + 2q = 13$ [1]
   $3p + 2q = 23$ [2]

7. $3y + z = 15$ [1]
   $4y + z = 17$ [2]

8. $g + 3h = 10$ [1]
   $4g + 3h = 22$ [2]

9. In question 5, what happens if you try to take [2] from [1] instead of taking [1] from [2]?

10. Copy down the following pair of equations and number them. Decide whether you should take the second from the first or the first from the second; then solve the equations.

$$4x + y = 21$$
$$5x + y = 26$$

Solve the following equations. Decide for yourself what to do first.

11. $2x + y = 6$
   $x + y = 4$

12. $5z + 2y = 19$
   $3z + 2y = 13$

13. $2p + q = 6$
   $7p + q = 21$

14. $9x + 2y = 28$
   $x + 2y = 12$

15. $a + 2b = 8$
   $2a + 2b = 14$

16. $3q + r = 14$
   $7q + r = 18$

17. $5x + 3y = 26$
   $x + 3y = 10$

18. $6a + c = 27$
   $3a + c = 21$

In some of the following questions, it is the first letter that will disappear, rather than the second.

19. $x + 2y = 11$ **22.** $3a + 2b = 20$

$x + y = 9$ $3a + b = 16$

20. $7p + 2q = 29$ **23.** $3x + 5y = 19$

$5p + 2q = 23$ $x + 5y = 13$

21. $2x + y = 17$ **24.** $x + 7y = 19$

$2x + 3y = 27$ $3x + 7y = 43$

EQUATIONS WITH A PLUS AND A MINUS SIGN

Consider the equations $3x + y = 5$ [1]

$2x - y = 10$ [2]

If we subtract $-y$ from y we get $y - (-y) = y + y = 2y$, so subtracting equation [2] from equation [1] gives $x + 2y = -5$, which does not help.

On the other hand if we *add* the two equations, y disappears

and we get $5x = 15$

EXERCISE 27e

Solve the pair of equations $2x + y = 10$

$x - y = 2$

$2x + y = 10$ [1]

$x - y = 2$ [2]

(This time we *add* the equations as $y + (-y) = 0$.)

[1] + [2] gives $3x = 12$

Divide both sides by 3 $x = 4$

(To find y it is easier to use the equation with the + sign.)

In [1], if $x = 4$, $8 + y = 12$

Take 8 from each side $y = 2$

Check in [2]: if $x = 4$ and $y = 2$, then $x - y = 2$
So $x = 4$ and $y = 2$.

Solve the following pairs of equations by adding the two equations. Remember to number them and to write down what you are doing.

1. $x + y = 7$

$x - y = 1$

4. $9a - b = 4$

$a + b = 6$

7. $3a - b = 14$

$2a + b = 16$

2. $2x + y = 16$

$x - y = 5$

5. $p + q = 8$

$7p - q = 32$

8. $5x + 2y = 26$

$3x - 2y = 6$

3. $2p - 3q = 9$

$p + 3q = 18$

6. $3y + 2z = 5$

$4y - 2z = 2$

9. $7x - y = 2$

$x + y = 6$

10. $a - b = 3$

$2a + b = 9$

12. $x - y = 2$

$5x + y = 22$

14. $5x + 3y = 18$

$x - 3y = 0$

11. $8g + 2h = 26$

$g - 2h = 1$

13. $2p - 3q = 12$

$2p + 3q = 12$

15. $a + 5c = 15$

$a - 5c = 5$

When solving a pair of equations,

if there are two plus signs, subtract
if there is a plus sign and a minus sign, add

EXERCISE 27f Solve the following pairs of equations. Decide whether you should add or subtract the equations.

1. $2x + y = 7$

$5x + y = 13$

4. $s + 2t = 10$

$5s - 2t = 2$

7. $a + b = 11$

$7a + b = 29$

2. $2x + 7y = 9$

$x + 7y = 8$

5. $5p + q = 6$

$3p + q = 6$

8. $3a + c = 18$

$a + c = 18$

3. $h - 3k = 2$

$h + 3k = 8$

6. $5p + q = 7$

$3p - q = 1$

9. $3a - c = 11$

$a + c = 5$

10. $5x + 2y = 29$ **13.** $7p + q = 14$ **16.** $3a - c = 1$

$x - 2y = 1$ $7p + 2q = 21$ $a + c = 7$

11. $5x + 2y = 9$ **14.** $7p + q = 13$ **17.** $2g + 2h = 16$

$x + 2y = 5$ $2p + q = 8$ $g - 2h = 2$

12. $5x - 2y = 0$ **15.** $7p + q = 8$ **18.** $4y + z = 28$

$x + 2y = 12$ $2p - q = 1$ $2y - z = 2$

19. An adult's bus fare is x pence and a child's is y pence. The total cost for two adults and one child is 60 p

so $2x + y = 60$

The cost for four adults and one child is £1.10, i.e. 110 pence,

so $4x + y = 110$

a) Solve the pair of equations.

b) What is the adult's fare and what is the child's are?

20. In a factory store room, there are x large boxes and y small ones. There are 40 boxes altogether, so $x + y = 40$

There are 16 more large boxes than small ones so $x - y = 16$

a) Solve the pair of equations.

b) How many large boxes are there and how many small ones?

MIXED EXERCISES

EXERCISE 27g 1. If $x + 2y = 14$ and $x = 6$ what is y?

2. Do $x = 1$ and $y = 2$ fit the pair of equations $2x + y = 4$

$x - y = 1$?

3. Solve the equations $p + 2q = 9$

$p - 2q = 5$

4. Give two possible pairs of solutions of the equation

$4x + y = 14$

5. Solve the equations $3x + 4y = 18$

$x + 4y = 14$

EXERCISE 27h **1.** If $2p + q = 11$ and $q = 3$, what is p?

2. Give two possible pairs of solutions of the equation

$$2a - b = 8$$

3. Solve the equations $\quad x + y = 11$

$$5x + y = 39$$

4. Solve the equations $\quad p - q = 2$

$$3p + q = 26$$

5. If $3x + 4y = 36$ and $y = 6$, what is x?

28

USING NEGATIVE NUMBERS IN EQUATIONS AND FORMULAE

WORKING WITH NEGATIVE NUMBERS

Remember that the rules for multiplying and dividing directed numbers are

> when the signs are the same, the answer is positive
> when the signs are different, the answer is negative,

i.e. $\qquad -2 \times -3 = 6 \quad$ and $\quad -(-4) = 4$

and $\qquad -2 \times 3 = -6$ and $2 \times (-3) = -6$

EXERCISE 28a Without using a calculator, find

1. $2 - (-3)$ **3.** $(-5)^2$ **5.** -5×4 **7.** $(-3)^2$

2. $4 \div (-2)$ **4.** $(-3) + (-2)$ **6.** $4 - (-1)$ **8.** $-6 \div (-2)$

USING NEGATIVE NUMBERS IN FORMULAE

EXERCISE 28b

If $c = a - b$, find c if $a = -2$ and $b = -4$

$$a = -2, \ b = -4$$
$$c = a - b$$
$$= (-2) - (-4)$$
$$= -2 + 4$$
$$= 2$$

374

1. If $a = b + c$, find a if $b = -4$ and $c = -2$

2. If $a = 2b + c$, find a if $b = -3$ and $c = -4$

3. If $x = y - z$, find x if $y = -4$ and $z = -1$

4. If $s = t - u$, find s if $t = -2$ and $u = 4$

5. If $p = 2q + r$, find p if $q = 4$ and $r = -1$

6. If $a = b - 3c$, find a if $b = -6$ and $c = 2$

7. If $x = 3y - 2z$, find x if $y = -2$ and $z = 5$

8. Find p when $x = 2$ and $y = -1$ given that $p = 2x - y$

9. Find T when $l = -2$ and $r = 4$ and $T = 3r + l$

10. Find V when $u = -4$ and $t = -5$ if $V = u + t$

11. If $a = b - 2c$ find a when $b = -4$ and $c = 5$

12. Given that $C = n - t$, find C when $n = 2.5$ and $t = -1$

NEGATIVE SOLUTIONS

Equations can have negative solutions. If we have an equation which is about temperatures, for instance, then we could have -3 as a solution. The temperature could be $-3\,°C$, i.e. 3 degrees below freezing point.

EXERCISE 28c

Solve the equation $x + 4 = 1$

$$x + 4 = 1$$

Take 4 from each side $\qquad x = 1 - 4$

$$x = -3$$

Solve the following equations.

1. $x + 5 = 2$	**4.** $z + 14 = 6$	**7.** $3 + x = 2$
2. $y + 9 = 8$	**5.** $r + 2 = 1$	**8.** $p + 3 = 1$
3. $6 + c = 2$	**6.** $x + 6 = 3$	**9.** $14 + y = 9$

10. $5 - x = 7$	**13.** $5 = 3 - c$	**16.** $2 = 1 - x$
11. $2 - a = 10$	**14.** $9 - s = 11$	**17.** $5 - x = 11$
12. $6 - q = 8$	**15.** $3 - x = 4$	**18.** $4 - x = 8$

19. The temperature at 6 a.m. was x °C. By 10 a.m. it had risen by 5° and the temperature was 3 °C.
The equation this gives is $x + 5 = 3$
Solve the equation.
What was the temperature at 6 a.m. ?

20. Sue started at floor x and used the lift to go up 4 floors.
She got out at floor 2.
The equation this gives is $x + 4 = 2$
Solve the equation.
What floor did she start from ?

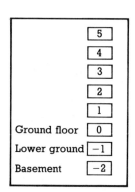

FINDING THE VALUE OF A LETTER ON THE RIGHT-HAND SIDE OF A FORMULA

We saw in chapter 10 that when we put numbers in the correct position in a formula, we get an equation to solve. Sometimes the solution is negative.

EXERCISE 28d

If $r = s + t$, find t if $r = -8$ and $s = -2$

$$r = -8, \quad s = -2$$
$$r = s + t$$
$$-8 = -2 + t$$

Add 2 to each side $\qquad -8 + 2 = t$

$$-6 = t$$

i.e. $\qquad\qquad\qquad t = -6$

---

1. If $x = y + z$, find y when $x = 4$ and $z = -2$

2. If $a = b + c$, find c when $a = -4$ and $b = 3$

3. If $p = q + r$, find q when $p = 6$ and $r = 9$

4. If $l = m + n$, find m when $n = -9$ and $l = -2$

5. If $s = t + u$, find u when $s = 7$ and $t = -2$

If $f = g - h$, find h if $f = -6$ and $g = -4$

$$f = -6, \quad g = -4$$
$$f = g - h$$
$$-6 = -4 - h$$

Add h to each side $\qquad -6 + h = -4$

Add 6 to each side $\qquad\quad h = -4 + 6$

$$= 2$$

6. If $p = r - q$, find r when $q = 4$ and $p = -7$

7. If $s = t - u$, find u when $s = 7$ and $t = -2$

8. If $x = y - z$, find y when $x = -2$ and $z = -3$

9. Give that $x = y - z$, find z if $x = 6$ and $y = -2$

10. If $p = q - r$, find q when $p = 4$ and $r = -2$

11. Given that $a = bc$, find c when $a = -12$ and $b = 3$

12. If $p = qr$, find q when $p = -12$ and $r = 6$

13. Given that $y = xz + 2$, find x when $y = -4$ and $z = 3$

MIXED EXERCISES

EXERCISE 28e 1. Given that $g = 2f + e$, find g when $f = -4$ and $e = 2$

2. If $p = 3q - r$, find q when $p = -8$ and $r = 2$

3. If $a = b(12 - c)$, find a when $b = 3$ and $c = 17$

4. Given that $a + b - 2 = c$,
a) find c when $a = 9$ and $b = 12$
b) find a when $b = 6$ and $c = 10$
c) find b when $a = 5$ and $c = 2$.

5. Using the formula $v = u + at$,
a) calculate the value of v if $u = 6.5$, $a = -4$ and $t = 3$
b) find the value of a when $v = 50$, $u = 2$ and $t = 6$

6. The formula $F = 1.8C + 32$ is used to convert temperature from degrees Celsius to degrees Fahrenheit.
a) Calculate F when $C = 25$
b) Find C when $F = 41$
c) Find the temperature in degrees Fahrenheit when a thermometer reads $-5\,°C$.

EXERCISE 28f In each question, several alternative answers are given. Write down the letter that corresponds to the correct answer.

1. If $x = y - z$, $y = 10$ and $z = 12$, then the value of x is

    A 2   **B** -2 **C** 120   **D** none of these

2. If $p = 2(q + r)$, $q = 7$ and $r = -3$, then the value of p is

    A 11   **B** 8   **C** 20   **D** 42

3. If $p = q + 2r$, $q = -2$ and $r = 3$, then the value of p is

    A 8   **B** -8 **C** 4   **D** -4

4. If $x = 3(y - z)$, $y = 4$ and $z = -1$, then the value of x is

    A 13   **B** 15   **C** 9   **D** 11

5. Given that $x = 2t - r$, $t = 3$ and $r = -2$, then the value of x is

    A 4   **B** 12   **C** 8   **D** -4

6. If $y = 12 - x$ and $x = -5$, the the value of y is

    A 17   **B** 60   **C** 7   **D** -7

29 MULTIPLE CHOICE REVISION EXERCISES

In all the exercises in this chapter, each question is followed by several alternative answers. Write down the letter that corresponds to the correct answer.

EXERCISE 1   ARITHMETIC

1.

The fraction of the figure that is shaded is

   A $\frac{1}{2}$ **B** $\frac{2}{5}$ **C** $\frac{1}{3}$ **D** $\frac{1}{5}$

2. Which one of the following numbers is prime?

   A 15   **B** 21   **C** 19   **D** 33

3. $2 + 3 \times 4$ is equal to

   A 14   **B** 20   **C** 9   **D** 11

4. 25% of 40 is

   A 4   **B** 20   **C** 25   **D** 10

5. The average of 1, 2, 2, 7 is

   A 2   **B** 4   **C** 3   **D** 5

6. The value of $3 - 1.9$ is

   A 1.1   **B** 2.1   **C** 2.9   **D** 1.6

7. The value of 2^5 is

   A 7   **B** 25   **C** 32   **D** 10

8. Which of the following numbers is the best rough estimate for $78.3 \div 5.17$?

   A 400   **B** 16   **C** 20   **D** 73

9.

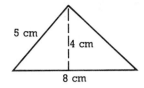

The area of this triangle is

A 32 cm²   **B** 20 cm²   **C** 16 cm²   **D** 40 cm²

10.

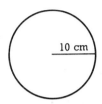

Taking π as approximately 3, the circumference of this circle is roughly

A 30 cm   **B** 60 cm   **C** 90 cm   **D** 15 cm

11. If 5 pens cost 50 p, 15 similar pens cost

    A 10 p   **B** £1.50   **C** 15 p   **D** none of these

12. The ratio 2 : 5 can be written as

    A 5 : 2   **B** 2.5 : 1   **C** 1 : 2.5   **D** 1 : 10

13. A shopkeeper gives a discount of 10% on marked prices. If the marked price of a radio is £30 what does he sell it for?

    A £33   **B** £27   **C** £40   **D** £20

14. The perimeter of one of the following figures cannot be found. Which one is it?

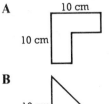

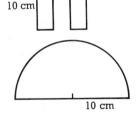

15. The profits of a company were shared between two partners in the ratio 2 : 3. The profits were £1500. The larger share was

    A £1000   **B** £900   **C** £300   **D** £600

EXERCISE 2   GEOMETRY

1.

The size of the angle
marked x is

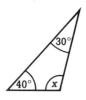

A 70°   **B** 110°   **C** 20°   **D** 290°

2.

The size of the angle
marked x is

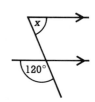

A 120°   **B** 30°   **C** 60°   **D** 90°

3.

The figure is a regular
hexagon. The size of the
angle marked x is

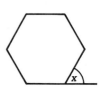

A 6°   **B** 120°   **C** 30°   **D** 60°

4.   One of the following regular figures will not tessellate.
Which one is it?

A   C

B   D

5. The number of lines of symmetry of an equilateral triangle is

A 3   **B** 6   **C** none   **D** 1

6.

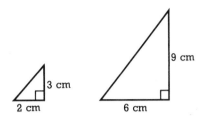

The triangle on the right is an enlargement of the triangle on the left. The scale factor is

A 1.5   **B** 2   **C** 4.5   **D** 3

7. Which one of the following statements about a parallelogram is *not* true?

A The opposite angles are equal.

B The diagonals are the same length.

C The opposite sides are the same length.

D Both pairs of opposite sides are parallel.

8. ABCDE is a pentagon. Which one of the following statements about ABCDE might *not* be true?

A The sum of the exterior angles is 360°.

B The figure has five sides.

C The figure has five lines of symmetry.

D The sum of the interior angles is 540°.

9. Which one of the following three statements about △ABC is *not* true?

A The area of ABC is 12 cm^2

B The length of AC is 5 cm

C $AB^2 + BC^2 = AC^2$

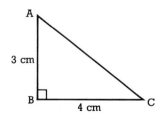

10. After a rotation about O of 180°, the image of this triangle is

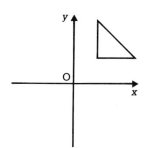

A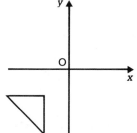

C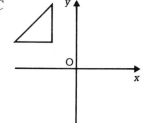

B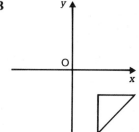

D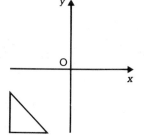

11. The grey triangle is produced by reflecting the black triangle in the

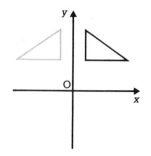

A x-axis   **B** y-axis   **C** line $y = 1$ **D** line $x = 1$

12.

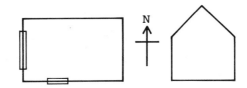

This is the plan and the east elevation of a shed. Which one of the following statements *cannot* be true?

A There is a window on the west side of the shed.

B There is a window on the south side of the shed.

C There is no window on the north side of the shed.

D There is a window on the east side of the shed.

EXERCISE 3   ALGEBRA AND PROBABILITY

1. $x + 2y + x$ can be written

    A $4x + y$ **B** $2x^2y$ **C** $4xy$ **D** $2x + 2y$

2. $2 + (x - 3)$ can be written

    A $x - 1$ **B** $5 + x$ **C** $2x - 6$ **D** $1 + x$

3. If $3x - 1 = 8$ then x is

    A $\frac{7}{3}$ **B** $\frac{1}{3}$ **C** 3   **D** 6

4. Given that $a = 2(b + c)$,   the value of a when $b = 3$ and $c = 2$ is

    A 10   **B** 12   **C** 8   **D** $2\frac{1}{2}$

5. The equation of a line is $y = 1 - 2x$.   When $x = -1$, y is

    A -1 **B** -2 **C** 3   **D** 1

6. $3(a - 2)$ can be written

    A $a - 6$ **B** $3a - 6$ **C** a **D** $3a - 2$

7. $x \times 2x$ can be written

    A $2x$ **B** $2x^2$ **C** $4x^2$ **D** $3x$

8.

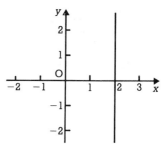

The equation of the line is

A $y = 2$ **B** $y = 0$ **C** $x + y = 2$ **D** $x = 2$

9. The graph of the line $y = x - 1$ is

A

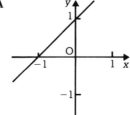

C

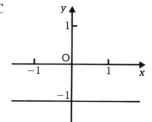

B

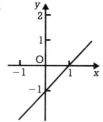

D

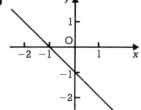

10. One disc is taken out of a bag containing five red discs and three blue discs. The probability that the disc is red is

A $\frac{1}{5}$ **B** $\frac{5}{3}$ **C** $\frac{1}{3}$ **D** $\frac{5}{8}$

11. This bar chart shows the number of books of various colours on a shelf.

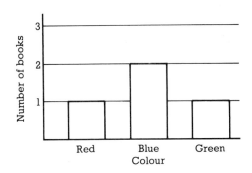

Which one of the following statements is correct?

A There are 3 books on the shelf.

B There is 1 red book on the shelf.

C The probability of picking a blue book from the shelf is $\frac{1}{3}$.

D More than half the books on the shelf are blue.

12. This is a sequence: 2, 5, 8, 11, . . .
The next two terms are

A 14, 17   **B** 12, 13   **C** 14, 18   **D** 19, 30